When life

M

CW01081873

This is a personal story of one women's inspiring journey to overcome kidney failure at just 20 years old. It shares the challenges of coping with kidney failure, dialysis treatment and transplantation, and how she and her family learnt to live with this new reality.

Helen Haynes was a promising sportswoman. She had big dreams - playing professional sport was one of them. Her determination and will to survive is evident throughout. It helps her rebuild her life, find new purpose and travel the world to support charitable causes and others less fortunate than herself.

Make it Count will inspire you to re-evaluate your own life and encourage you to make the most of every day.

'It is very exciting to see Helen's book come to life after the germination of the project two decades ago! Helen is an inspiring and passionate person from whom we can all learn a great deal about tackling life – and the severest of setbacks – with a positive, committed attitude, thereby turning hardship into success.'

- Lindiwe Dovey

'I never doubted Helen's strength to overcome any adversity and it has been done so with aplomb! I know you will enjoy Helen's book. It is amusing, brutally honest, filled with enthusiasm and refreshing, as is Helen!'

- Peter Miles, former Headmaster Hudson Park High School,
South Africa

'I applaud Helen's inspirational determination to succeed whatever the challenge and I know the message of her book will help others to overcome adversity and go for whatever it is they want out of their lives.'

- Wendy Yorke, Book Coach and friend

'Helen is a true source of positive energy. Her passion for charity, her power to connect with people from all works of life and her determination to change the lives of young people is awe inspiring. She quite literally changes people's lives.'

- Becky Cragg, a former charity colleague

'Helen Haynes is a unique, stoic character, mentally equipped to conquer a life-threatening situation, blessed with loving support. Hers is an inspiring story.'

- Peter Kirsten, Former Western Province, Border,
South African International Cricketer

'Helen's infectious passion motivates and encourages me to explore my own ambitions. I always know who to turn to for a cup of Guidance and Wisdom (and a slice of cake to help digest it!).'

- Louise Scott, charity fundraising professional

About the Author

Helen Haynes, born in East London, South Africa, has achieved international success as a professional speaker, charity fundraiser and most recently as a businesswoman. Her passion to make a difference in the world came about after facing life-threatening kidney failure at just 20. It ended her promising sporting career, changed her perspective and taught her compassion and strength.

Using her determined and positive spirit, Helen has raised millions for charities in South Africa, Australia and the United Kingdom. She now empowers professionals to share their message with passion and power through her public speaking, coaching and training business. Helen is also an avid and inspiring speaker, sharing her life lessons in her unique relaxed style with candour and humour.

Helen lives with her husband, Glen, and dog, Jasper, and splits her time between England and Australia.

A promising sporting career
shattered by kidney failure.
When life gives you a second chance...

Make it Count!

An inspiring journey of
triumph over adversity.

Helen Haynes

Published by
Filament Publishing Ltd
16, Croydon Road, Waddon, Croydon,
Surrey, CR0 4PA, United Kingdom
Telephone +44 (0)20 8688 2598
Fax +44 (0)20 7183 7186
info@filamentpublishing.com
www.filamentpublishing.com

© Helen Haynes 2014

The right of Helen Haynes to be identified as the author
of this work has been asserted by her in accordance with the
Designs and Copyright Act 1988.

ISBN - 978-1-910125-33-5

Printed by Berforts Information Press
Stevenage & Hastings

This book is subject to international copyright and may
not be copied in any way without the prior written
permission of the publishers.

Cover Photography by Simon Hooley of The Image Cella

Mom - this one's for you!

Thank you for giving me

the incredible gift of life.

With all my love and gratitude.

Contents

Foreword

Occasionally on life's journey we meet someone who makes a lasting impression. Helen is such a person. I was privileged to be part of the team which cared for her during the darkest days of her illness. Her inner strength and remarkable resilience were the characteristics which enabled her to face the many crises she encountered at a young age. Most transplants are largely uneventful. The course of Helen's illness and subsequent management are best described as 'stormy'. However, she remained hopeful and strong as she faced each new setback. I trust that her story will inspire many who face similar challenges in their lives.

– Mervyn Griffiths
Consultant Physician

1

A Sporting Chance

'Life is a succession of lessons which must be lived to be understood.'

– Helen Keller

I was nineteen years old and I felt like a failure. As I gazed out the plane window, I shuddered at the thought of what I was going to say to everyone. What on earth was I going to do with the rest of my life? Just fifteen months earlier, everything had looked so rosy. Years of dedicated training and single-minded focus had won me a tennis scholarship to the USA. I'd been all fired up to work hard and make it big, perhaps even get to Wimbledon. But now, playing international tennis was looking very unlikely. I had blown it. I was coming home to South Africa with very little to show for a year in Louisiana pursuing my dreams.

The ground sped underneath us as the plane landed smoothly on the runway of East London Airport. After a deep breath to settle my butterflies, I stepped out into the South African sunshine. I could see Mom and Dad standing in the terminal and on either side of them my younger siblings, Michelle and Peter. Wow, they had grown so much. We were all a little shy and with stilted questions we tried to fill the gaps of our time apart.

Dad drove home along the beachfront and I marvelled at how different East London looked even after just a year and a bit away. Though the city was popular with holidaymakers, it had always been very family-oriented as well – a really nice place to grow up. Now, new developments had replaced parklands and while some buildings had modernised, others seemed decidedly outdated. Everything was on such a small scale compared to the US.

Mitzi, my white Maltese poodle, was waiting at the window of our home as if nothing had changed. She bounced around excitedly when I stepped inside with my luggage. I regretted having left her behind for so long. Our large black cat, Kitty, slunk into the kitchen and purred when I picked him up for a cuddle.

'Hello, sis!' Thelma was just as excited to see me. She had been our live-in maid forever and was very much part of the family. With typical African directness,she waved her arms at my now chubbier figure and added, 'Woah, you big girl now!'

It was good to be home. Back in the family fold. After my year overseas, I was physically and mentally exhausted and I was going to need all the support I could get.

*

Nearly two years before, I received the call that changed my life. It was the summer of 1988. Outside, a bitter storm lashed and I listened to the trees groaning against the wind. I pulled the duvet right up to my chin while Mitzi whimpered and nudged to get under the covers.

The sound of the telephone interrupted my fractured sleep. The luminous green digits of my clock radio flashed 2 a.m. as I stumbled out of bed and ran to the phone. Who would call at this time? Had something happened?

My heart throbbed in my ears as my voice wavered. 'Hi. Helen speaking.'

There was a hollow silence at the other end. Was this a prank call? Dad, a light sleeper, emerged from behind his bedroom door with a questioning look.

I waited on the line and watched the rest of the family form a comical, pyjama-clad coterie around me. No one said a word.

Suddenly out of the crackle, 'Hey there, this is Coach Todd from Louisiana. Is that Helen?'

That was one extreme southern drawl and I realised it was the tennis coach from one of the universities I had applied to a couple of months earlier.

'Yes it is,' I gasped.

'I hope y'all been practising, Helen?'

I mouthed to my family that it was a coach from America and the faces around me brightened. They all began to whisper at once.

'It's from America!'

'Could it be about a scholarship?'

'Sssshhhh! I want to listen!'

I couldn't believe what Todd was saying. Could it be true? Mom was hurriedly writing down questions on bits of paper. I was struggling to take it all in.

'Thanks, Todd. Sounds great! I look forward to receiving the forms and will send them back as soon as I can.'

I couldn't contain my excitement as I banged the receiver down.

'I got it! He offered me a full tennis scholarship to start next year. He said he looks forward to seeing me in September. I am going to America! Can you believe that? Where's a map? I need to remind myself where Louisiana is!'

Laughing, Mom grabbed the atlas off the shelf and we scanned the States. There was the boot-shaped state way down south and parallel to Florida. I knew nothing about the area, only what I had read in Huckleberry Finn's adventures on the Mississippi. Texas was close by and I recognised the infamous city of Dallas.

At last I could tell my friends that I was leaving for sure. I don't think anyone really believed me when I said I was trying to secure a tennis or hockey scholarship so that I could study in America. It was the only way I could further my sporting career. Because of its apartheid policy, South Africa was heavily sanctioned and we were banned from competing in the Olympics. Our political situation was preventing international success in so many ways. I just knew I had to leave to make it. America would be my land of opportunity.

'I guess there goes the idea of a hockey scholarship to Ohio, hey?'

I looked at Mom and Dad as I realised that my toughest decision had been made for me in a single moment. Tennis would be my future.

*

A passion for sport ran in the family. Mom and Dad met on the squash court and sport was an integral part of my childhood. My earliest memories are of spending long hours with my parents at the sports club, hitting tennis balls with friends against the wall behind the clubhouse and playing mini hockey with the other children. Dad played top-level tennis, hockey, squash, cricket and even ran marathons - he was a real all-round sportsman. Mom was a promising swimmer and later a hockey player who would have made the Springbok team had her knees not let her down and replacement forced her to retire. She went on to manage county teams and became president of Border Hockey, our region, as well as a representative on the national committee in the junior and senior sections.

My parents instilled in me a strong love of sport and for that I will always be grateful. Once at school, I discovered gymnastics. The pleasure I got from performing, posing and achieving perfection in a move was addictive. Other gymnasts became my best friends and we would spend hours tumbling on mats in the school hall and creating performances for family *braai* (barbecue) parties at home. Our coach taught us that you never give up. Keep trying, keep working hard and eventually you will have success. She was a hard task-master but supportive and encouraging. As eight-year-olds, my friend Gaye and I spent many afternoons giggling in the corner. The punishment was more beam work or swinging on the bars.

Modern dance was added to my weekly schedule to improve my rhythm on the floor and, again, this was all about performance and flexibility. Ballet proved less conducive. I was told I was better suited to gymnastics because I couldn't stop sticking my bottom and chest out – a classic gymnastics pose at the end of a routine.

My dream was to compete for my country at the Olympic Games. Nadia Comaneci and Olga Korbut were my idols. But when tennis and hockey started making more demands on my time, I faced a difficult choice. Despite my love of tumbling and the fun of entering lots of national competitions, gymnastics offered limited opportunities for a South African. Resources were restricted and we were barred from the Olympics. Also, for most people, a career as a gymnast is fairly short-lived. Few compete beyond their teenage years. The body just can't handle the stress.

Gymnastics with friends (from left) Penny, Kim, me,
Karen, Lynne and Gaye

My parents were always so encouraging and supportive of my sporting pursuits. They helped me believe that I was good enough to achieve my goals in gymnastics and this fuelled my passion for the sport. It was only later that I discovered I really wasn't that good. But because I loved it so much, Mom and Dad let me enjoy the experience and compete on a national level, even if it meant coming bottom of the pile.

When I think back to the times I struggled with physical injuries and illness, the signs that my body was not going to cope with intensive training were already apparent at a young age. I developed tonsillitis before just about every gym competition: my stress flared up in my throat. Antibiotics did not agree with me; I had allergic reactions to anything linked to penicillin. My joints would swell up and I would develop hives all over my body. Eventually my tonsils were removed and years later, because a part of my left tonsil was left behind by the surgeon, I had to have one of them removed again! Such luck.

At the age of eleven I made my primary school first teams in both hockey and tennis and soon my gymnastics dreams were forgotten. I practised hard, my parents invested in private tennis coaching and I started fitness training.

Mom was my hockey coach and cheering squad. She spent many cold and windy afternoons shouting from the sidelines at my school and club matches. Dad encouraged and supported my tennis. It became an interesting balancing act throughout my high-school career as I split my time between the two sports. I achieved fairly equally in both. In reality, I was probably a better hockey player and loved nothing more than to score goals as a centre forward. I worked hard to perfect my skills, despite hating the thought of being hit by the ball or stick. Fear can make you very quick and nifty.

At the age of fifteen, I made the state teams in both sports and the goal was always to play for my country. I came close with hockey, being chosen for the South African hockey training squad, but shin splints really knocked my confidence and affected my training and performance.

Little did I know what chaos shin splints would cause in my life.

Scoring goals with my hockey friend, Pam.

Hockey - South African B team in 1988. I am 4th from the right in the top row, next to my friend Pam.

Shin splints is the term given to pain in the front of your legs along the shin bone. It is a common and agonising injury that's sustained after excessive training or when playing a sport that involves a lot of stop/starts, such as tennis. There are a number of causes but mostly it comes from intense pressure on the legs. My shin splints flared up after a combination of lots of sprint training, indoor hockey on tennis courts and aerobics during tennis practice while wearing just regular tennis shoes and on a surface that was not suitable for this sort of fitness training.

Tennis, I believed, was the way to achieve my dreams. I loved the game. I might not have been the best, but I was determined, hardworking and had a fair amount of talent to get me where I wanted to go. Between the ages of twelve and eighteen, my holidays were spent travelling all around South Africa, playing in tennis tournaments with my friends. It was a lot of fun, particularly when we stayed in small towns and had to fend for ourselves for dinners and transport to the courts.

In 1987, when I was seventeen and coming to the end of high school, I began researching what it would take to win a scholarship to America. The chance to travel, expand my horizons and compete on an international stage were vital to reaching my goals. Most of my friends were applying to universities in South Africa. I knew this was an option for me, but I was determined to go overseas. It was something I had to do. My focus in my last few years of school was on sport first, studying second. I did everything I could to be in the best shape possible. I read books and followed sporting stars, learning how they trained, what they ate, how they behaved. Very few mornings began without a training run, game of tennis or hockey practice in the winter. Because I lived in a country where the sun got up early almost all year round, I made the most of it. School started at 7.30 a.m. so I woke at 5 a.m. if necessary to fit in my training. School finished at 2 p.m., which left me at least four hours to train or practise with friends. If there was no squad practice at school or with our county teams, I arranged tennis games with friends. I needed to play every day.

While my friends spent their Friday or Saturday nights at Numbers, our local dance club, I went to bed early so that I could handle squad practice in the morning or league matches the following day. My sport came first. I am sure my friends thought I was pretty boring. I found that I had two sets of friends: those that played sport and those that didn't. Between them they provided the friendship, support and balance I needed at the time. In the final two years of school I befriended a mixed group of high achievers and most of us became prefects.

I captained both my tennis and hockey teams and developed my leadership and motivational skills to great effect. I loved nothing more than to lead my team to victory and encourage enthusiasm and passion.

When the call came in from Todd that fateful early morning in 1988, I knew my hard work had paid off. But my year in Louisiana didn't go as well as I'd hoped. My health, fitness levels and enthusiasm all took a nose-dive. The reason I had eventually decided to come home was because I was feeling unwell, but there didn't seem to be anything specific apart from a sore neck, frequent headaches and tiredness. If Dad hadn't said, 'Just come home,' I would have ploughed on, happy or not.

I often say, 'If only I knew then, what I know now.' We make choices in life that we believe will take us where we want to go, but sometimes they take us off the path we are meant to be on. Hindsight is a wonderful thing and it is easy to judge ourselves on decisions or choices we make. Signs of ill-health show up in all sorts of ways. Knowing yourself, your body and how you should feel is the first step to being able to spot the signs when things are going wrong inside. My only excuse is that I was young and naive. In truth, despite being so focused on fitness, health and improving my skills, I was not fully rounded in my approach to the goals I was working towards.

2
The End of Life as I Knew It

'We must be willing to let go of the life we planned so as to have the life that is waiting for us.'

- Joseph Campbell

With my tennis dreams unfulfilled and feeling confused about my career, I was back in East London wondering what to do with myself. For the first time in my life I felt depressed and lacked motivation. I was overweight, unhappy and felt completely lost. I was barely able to drag myself out of bed each day. Something was wrong, but I couldn't put my finger on it. Maybe I just needed to toughen up and pull myself together. I could tell Mom and Dad were concerned – my lack of enthusiasm was totally out of character – but they weren't aware of the full extent of my malaise.

Before flying home, I had been on a three-week Greek adventure holiday with friends. Even then I had noticed the headaches and nausea. One morning I even vomited after breakfast. Strange and random. I did visit a local doctor in London on my way back to South Africa. She took a urine sample (my first ever) and diagnosed a pulled muscle in my neck. Rest and painkillers were all she suggested and I vaguely remember her saying to the receptionist that there was blood and protein in my urine. 'We'll call you when the tests come back' was the last I heard. I never got the results.

Sleeping off the headaches wasn't working. Keeping a low profile, I spent my days in and out of our swimming pool while my family were at school or work. If I hadn't been feeling so rough, it would have been a nice break. We were living close to the beach at the time, in a large house with a swimming pool and an expansive garden in which the family often played cricket, football and table tennis.

Dad gave me a part-time job at Taylors Sports. He was director of this family-owned sports store in East London and even though we didn't own the business it had always been a part of our lives. The job got me out of the house and gave me something to focus on other than the exhaustion and nausea.

I also visited our family doctor and just about managed to stop him from fobbing me off with a scribbled prescription and a joke about hypochondria. After listening to my vague symptoms, he surmised that I was probably in need of a good rest. The heavy year of tennis, travel and training had obviously taken its toll.

'But I have been resting and it hasn't helped!' I squeaked, holding back the tears.

'It looks like you could be suffering from jetlag and you have a touch of hypertension.'

Seriously? How long does jetlag last? And hypertension? Why would I have high blood pressure? Then I remembered that during a routine check-up in Louisiana the university medical officer had mentioned slightly elevated blood pressure. No treatment had been suggested then and nothing had been done.

A couple of weeks after my visit to the family doctor the vomiting began. It happened in the morning, just after I woke up. As a young girl training to get fit, I used to love my morning runs with Dad, branding dark footprints in the dew together while the city slept around us. Now mornings were fast losing their appeal. I worried that Mom and Dad would think I was pregnant because it seemed so like morning sickness (although I didn't quite believe in divine conception!). I tried not to make a big deal of the vomiting and became an expert at throwing up quickly, brushing my teeth and carrying on as normal. No one suspected a thing. Towards lunchtime the nausea normally abated and I would risk testing my stomach with a snack.

I was very frustrated. It was really hard to work out what to do with my life when I felt so awful. Then Ray Suttner, the director of Rhodes University in East London, came to my rescue. He was a family friend and he was certain he could assist. He listened to my thoughts about my future and we discussed my options. It was so refreshing to have someone other than my parents take an interest. And I loved his exuberant sense of humour and the cheeky laugh he concealed beneath his moustache.

Thanks to his confidence in my abilities, I became excited at the thought of starting to study once more. I would begin a Business Commerce degree in February of the following year, reuniting with my friends who were now a couple of years ahead of me. Ray also offered me a job in the newly formed Sports Administration Department of the university, working alongside the South African cricketer Peter Kirsten. The work would be a form of scholarship and would give me experience within the field of sports administration, which is what I was keen to do.

I started the job straight away and began a daily routine of commuting between Taylors Sports and Rhodes University. Bored with rest, I even began playing tennis again and tried to build up my fitness. Painkillers suppressed the headaches, but the nausea was more challenging. At my Rhodes job I would became hot and sweaty before a nausea attack and would force myself to walk sedately out of the office before sprinting to get to the bathrooms in time. I tried skipping breakfast in the morning to curb the nausea.

In spite of my thinking it was all so *obvious*, still no one suspected a thing. I chose to keep as much of it to myself as I could so as not to worry my parents and to avoid any fuss. I was still able to work, play tennis and go out with friends so if I ignored the start of the day and the exhaustion, which had become 'normal', then I could manage. It was all very weird. Who vomited every morning and then carried on the rest of the day? Not only was it vile, but slightly embarrassing too.

I was also trying hard to shift the significant amount of weight I had gained during my year overseas. I experimented with Weigh-less, Fit for Life and any other diet I discovered, but nothing worked. Instead I felt sicker.

I was not so friendly the second time I visited our family doctor. It was over a month since the first visit and I was fed up. I was emotional and unhappy and begged him to help me. He took a urine sample and I remember wondering what you could possibly find out by examining someone's wee. He immediately noticed an abnormality on the urine dipstick and announced that I had a kidney infection.

'What?' I exclaimed. 'A kidney infection? But why would I have that?'

'There is nothing to panic about, Helen. It should clear with a dose of antibiotics.'

I left with a prescription for *more* pills and instructions to drink plenty of water. A *kidney* infection? It sounded disgusting! But Mom and Dad were relieved that we finally had a label to attach to my ongoing malaise. They had been surprised to learn that I was still struggling after all this time. Being home had not helped yet. They put me to bed (again!) and told me to rest from work and sport for a while. Maybe I hadn't rested enough when I first came home?

After a few days of forced rest I was restless once more. I picked up a racquet again and began taking lessons with a professional coach, Grant, in an attempt to revive my flagging tennis. I had known Grant since school, when we had trained in the Border squad together, but we only became friends when I got back from America. We started spending a lot of time together, which was both distracting and enjoyable.

The coaching paid off and I was selected to play for our local team in the annual interstate tennis competition, the Grand Challenge, in Stutterheim. Dad drove our team minibus while I gazed out at the smooth, picturesque hills dotted with straw-roofed rondavel huts typical of this region. I'd only had an apple for breakfast but I could feel the nausea building. Deep breathing and swallowing wasn't working and I soon threw up. Everyone was fussing and Dad was probably more embarrassed and concerned than I was. I wondered if the kidney infection was still hanging around.

The weekend got progressively worse. When I walked on to the court for my doubles match the white lines glared up at me in the way they do when you haven't played tennis for a long time. During the warm-up I felt leaden and disorientated. My partner gave me a sideways glance, but I didn't have the energy to respond. How could I explain how I was feeling? I was under pressure to perform. Everyone was expecting great things from me following my American tennis experience.

We won the toss and selected to serve. The balls were placed in my hand and I walked haltingly to the backline. I double-faulted. I double-faulted again. Finally I served one in and then hit an uncontrolled shot into the net. One more double-fault followed.

'One love!' our opponents announced, as if we didn't know.

My game did not improve: instead it got progressively worse. I felt shaky. I had no power, couldn't serve, couldn't concentrate and felt so bad for my partner and for my dad. He was sitting in the clubhouse with Grant, his eyes pleading with me to save him from having to answer questions about the state of my tennis.

Embarrassed and shattered, I wanted to hide under a rock and cry. My performance had been a disaster and on the way home I made a secret pact to hide from the tennis world. Never again did I want to be humiliated like that.

But the overriding emotion I felt was fear. There was something horribly wrong with me, I was sure of it.

*

It took our family doctor three appointments over three months to come to a half-realisation of the seriousness of my condition. On the third visit Mom came with me and took charge. She demanded a blood test and we were told that we would hear in a few days.

I gave no thought to the impending results and spent the following day accompanying my boss on a work trip to Grahamstown, a university town two hours' drive from East London. When we got back to the office, I was given a message that Dad wanted me to stop off and see him at the tennis club before I went home. This was unusual. What could be so important that it couldn't wait till I saw him later? I tried to rationalise and keep calm. Maybe he needed a lift, or wanted me to buy something for supper, or needed me to collect Peter from a friend's? None of us had mobile phones in those days, so I couldn't just call and ask him directly.

Dad ran off the court as soon as he saw my car descend the steep road to the clubhouse. He asked distractedly how my trip had been. I could tell that there was something more he wanted to say.

'You left a message, Dad. What's wrong?'

'The doctor rang and said he's booked a bed for you at St Dominic's.'

'What do you mean, he's booked a bed at St Dominic's?'

'Your blood results weren't good and he wants to run more tests. They have been waiting for you all day. We couldn't get hold of you.'

'But why can't I just have the tests done tomorrow? Why hospital?'

'I don't know, Helly Bells. I think they want to find out what's going on.'

I couldn't argue with that, but this was ridiculous. What difference would one day make? The urgency didn't make sense. I felt unwell, but not bad enough to need hospital – and tonight? I was just walking around as normal.

I drove home in a state of panic, fear and frustration. As much as I wanted to feel better, I was also scared of what the doctors might find. 'Hospital' sounded so serious. By the time I reached the house I was sufficiently composed to help Mom pack some things in a small overnight bag. I tried to put on a brave face. The last place in the world I wanted to go to was a hospital.

By the time Dad was back from tennis, Mom and I were ready to leave. There was nothing any of us could say. It was very strange and unsettling. There was a feeling of dread hanging over me as we drove into the hospital car park.

And so on 1 November 1990, at the age of twenty, my life in the medical world began.

3
'Bean' Different

'I can be changed by what happens to me. But I refuse to be reduced by it.'

– Maya Angelou

I slept very badly that first night in St Dominic's. I felt like crying when my family went home after visiting hours. I wanted to go home to my bed too. The only reason I kept up my brave display was because I happened to know the woman who was sharing my two-bed ward. Doreen was the mother of an old schoolfriend of mine. She had just had an operation to fix her spine and was flat on her back. At least I was still free to walk around and go to the toilet.

However, going to the loo quickly became a big issue and not a very private one. I was ordered to tell the nurses exactly what and how much I drank. They then measured every drop of my urine. Weeing into a jug was a whole new experience. Castor oil for breakfast was the worst start to my first day in hospital. What kind of punishment was that? How I managed to swallow the vile yellow goo I don't know; I nearly spat it all over the bed.

By late morning there was still no sign of a doctor. I wanted to know what my blood results were and why they had caused so much panic. I was still clueless as to what was going on. Eventually a nurse told me that my doctor had gone on a hike. He had left on the same day that I was admitted into St Dominic's Hospital. I was going to be referred to a specialist instead.

The specialist assigned to my case was short and stocky and had a robust sense of humour that brightened the dreary surrounds. He immediately barked orders at the staff around my bed and instructed that I be placed on a special diet, making the already tasteless hospital cuisine even less appealing. As he answered some of my questions it became clear that he was concerned about my kidneys. The words 'creatinine' and 'urea' were part of the new vocabulary I was fast beginning to learn. Creatinine is muscle waste that the kidneys are responsible for eliminating from the body. If your creatinine stays high, this means your kidneys are not working properly. Urea is a waste product formed from the breakdown of protein and is usually passed out in the urine. I didn't really understand the significance of this information at that point. The specialist said he was not sure how damaged my kidneys were, why they were not functioning properly or what the problem was. To me it sounded like the medics knew nothing.

As a new kidney patient I had many adjustments to make and the first one was getting over my embarrassment. I tried to come up with appropriate phrases for my various bodily functions but soon gave up. How I wished that my problem involved something other than the excretory system.

I was introduced to the 'vampires' on my second day in hospital. They were dressed in chic navy suits and carried little black boxes filled with the latest technological equipment for blood extraction – tubes, syringes and pain! My very own duo of Dracula's assistants were from the Blood Bank laboratory. How I loathed those needles.

An array of coloured glass tubes landed on my bed, ready to be filled. One of the vampires selected a needle – the largest, or so it seemed to me – and I scrunched up my hand while she punctured my arm. Aagh, she was taking her time. I couldn't look.

'Just relax, my dear. It will all be over in a minute.'

I am not your 'dear', I thought, as I watched a fly buzzing around the window ledge. I knew how the poor fly felt, trapped in that awful place.

'Will I faint from losing all that blood?' I asked as she placed yet another tube of my blood on the bed.

My enquiry fell on deaf ears. The second vampire handed her colleague tube after tube and they chatted to one another with absolutely no concern for my whinging or stress.

Once they had left me in peace, the afternoon dragged on and I wished my doctor would come back and say I could go home. But I wasn't to see him until the following morning. He brought more bad news.

The results of the tests were similar to those that had prompted my GP to admit me to hospital in the first place; there had been no improvement in my kidney function. I had less than 20 per cent kidney function, a creatinine level of 720 (normal is between 80 and 120), a critical potassium level (dangerous for my heart, I later learnt) and everything else was completely out of synch. I felt a bizarre sense of relief that they had discovered what was wrong with me. Finally someone was taking me seriously: the tiredness, nausea, headaches and lack of concentration were no longer simply figments of my imagination.

I was told my kidneys would deteriorate further if more drastic treatment wasn't tried. My St Dominic's specialist said he needed support with my 'beans' – the term which we all quickly came to use for my kidneys – and referred me to another renal specialist at the larger state-run Frere Hospital nearby. I was in no mood to meet another doctor but I agreed and was discharged to take the next step on my journey to recovery.

*

Dr G met me and my parents at the renal clinic on the first floor of Frere Hospital in East London. He ushered us into a small consulting room with an examination bed on one side, a desk in the middle and three chairs in front of it. He pulled a fourth chair in from the corridor. There was a chart with letters of the alphabet on one wall and a few notices, including one with a bold Aids warning on another. I remember looking at the chart and making sure I could read all the letters to the bottom line. This became a habit every time I met with him in that room. It gave me relief and satisfaction knowing that I could at least see. He spoke quickly and softly and made sure we were comfortable. With his greying hair and serious, caring demeanour he seemed older than my two previous doctors. His passion for his specialism was evident and I immediately warmed to him.

After listening to my experiences of the last few months, Dr G scribbled notes illegibly on a large notepad. His brow crinkled into sympathetic lines as we relayed the events leading up to my admittance to hospital. My voice was shaky and I struggled to keep my composure. Was it really me we were talking about? I was scared and feeling emotional. Dr G shook his head and sighed compassionately. He questioned me thoroughly and I was forced to recall the year I spent in America.

'Were you in any accidents or falls?' he asked.

'Not that I can remember. I had so many other injuries though.'

'Did you? Like what?'

I shifted in my chair as I mentioned the years of shin splints and how they had become really bad while I was training. I told him about the many hours I had spent in the sports treatment room at the university in Louisiana. How I was taped up in bandages from knees to toes before tennis, just so that I could bear to step onto the court. I also mentioned the niggling tendonitis in my right elbow and ankle.

'Did you take anything for these injuries?'

'Sometimes. Nothing worked, but I used to take these little white tablets which were given to us for most ailments.'

'They must have been some sort of painkiller. Can you remember what they contained?'

'I never asked. I was just told to take two before practice, and whenever I felt pain. Many of the athletes took them and we were also recommended to take them for flu, sore throats and headaches. They were the miracle pills all of us athletes used in order to cope with the heavy training schedules.'

I wasn't going to mention that the trainers recommended them to us as an excellent cure (or even preventive measure) for hangovers. This had been quite handy when practice was at 7 a.m. on a Saturday.

Dr G was writing frantically and looking very concerned. I started to wonder where this was leading.

'Do you remember how many you took?'

Why was he still asking about those stupid pills?

'I have no idea. I didn't take them every day. I had a lot of headaches and the pain in my shins was unbearable on most days. Even walking hurt!' I was starting to feel like a guilty child.

'Would you say a bottle? Two? Three?'

'Over the year?'

He nodded.

'Probably a few bottles.'

'And there would have been a hundred pills in each bottle?'

'I'm not sure. Fifty or a hundred probably.'

'Have you got a sample with you?'

I had none left, but couldn't remember seeing any instructions or ingredients written on the bottle anyhow. What did all this concern about the pills have to do with my kidneys?

We agreed that I would try and get a bottle of the pills from America if I could. Dr G continued to ask about my medical history, my allergies and anything else we could remember that might help us understand what had caused this unexpected kidney problem.

Mom asked a few more questions while Dad sat listening intently, trying to keep a brave face like me. I found the whole situation overwhelming. How had things gone so wrong? Who would have thought kidneys were so important? In fact, this was the first time in my twenty years that I had given them so much as a second thought.

After extracting every piece of information he could from us, Dr G confirmed that a biopsy was definitely the next step. His words dropped on me like a ton of bricks. This was the moment I had been dreading. I had found out from the nurses at St Dominic's that a biopsy was pretty painful and I'd been secretly hoping he could diagnose me without this torturous test.

'Are you sure there is no other way?'

'Sorry, no. You have acute kidney failure. I need to take a sample of your kidneys to find out what is causing this. We can then treat you effectively.'

I was not impressed. He drew a graph to demonstrate how my creatinine was escalating and it was evident that I had far from normal kidney function. As I now knew, one of the best ways to monitor kidney function is through levels of creatinine and urea, both of which are filtered by the kidneys. If your kidneys aren't working properly these levels rise in the blood. If your blood is not cleaned properly, substances like this form poisons in your body and cause damage to other organs like the heart. My creatinine was extremely high.

Normally a person with my levels of creatinine and urea would be prepped for dialysis immediately, but we were still unsure what was causing my kidney problem and Dr G needed to investigate further to see if there was another possible treatment option. My biopsy was booked for the following day – far too soon for my liking.

On the way home we tried to digest and make sense of the latest news. Dr G was in no doubt that I had acute kidney failure. Never in our worst nightmares had we imagined this happening to someone in our family. The reality that I could be extremely ill was slowly dawning on us as Dad turned the car into our driveway. How could we begin to explain something like that to my brother and sister?

You never realise how strong you are until you are put to the test. This was most definitely my test for now. Facing a diagnosis of any illness is challenging, but what was making this even more difficult for me was the fact that we still didn't really have a cause and there was no clear treatment plan. I most certainly wasn't ready to digest the prognosis. Nothing like this had ever occurred in our family so there was little to reference. We were expecting this 'kidney thing' to go away as fast as it had arrived in our lives. But we had no such luck.

4
Facing My Fears

'I don't run away from a challenge because I am afraid. Instead, I run towards it because the only way to escape fear is to trample it beneath your foot.'

- Nadia Comaneci

My childhood was mostly safe and secure and free from fear. There were probably only a handful of times when I had felt real fear. Like the time I was chased by a raging crazy man on the clifftops at Hole-in-the-Wall on the Wild Coast. I am not sure if he wanted to hurt me or just rob me, but I remember running for my life, hearing my heart in my ears and feeling my lungs burn in my chest from the exertion. Gymnastics brought a different fear, especially during competitions on the beam. Willing myself to try death-defying somersaults or stay on that tiny plank of wood while I did forward rolls and walkovers took all my strength as a ten-year-old. It also toughened me up and taught me the value of self-belief, the power of the mind. I quickly learnt that with focus and concentration I was able to achieve so much more than I expected.

But fear of the future? That was a fear like no other I had experienced before. My life up to this point had been filled with positive goals, dreams and aspirations. Now I was in turmoil. Tearing away at me was my dread of needles, hospitals and all things medical, along with my fear of the unknown. What did my future hold?

*

Mom drove me back to Frere Hospital the morning after our meeting with Dr G. The ugly grey stone building that had held a curious fascination for me in earlier years was becoming strangely familiar. The strong antiseptic smell that lingered in the corridors made me feel sick. Dr G had already booked a bed for me in the general 'Female Medical' ward. There were twelve identical beds in the ward and nine of them were occupied. The drugged-looking faces of the sleeping women were of little comfort to my churning insides.

The ward sister guided us to my bed in the corner and while Mom unpacked my things into the little cubicle, I changed into the starched pale blue hospital nightgown with its broken girdle. I wondered how many people had worn it before me. It felt scratchy and uncomfortable and I wished I could wear my own nightie.

Soon a porter arrived to take me down for the biopsy. He had brought a wheelchair. At first I didn't understand and tried to object.

'I am sure I can manage to walk down myself,' I said, embarrassed.

'Sorry, madam,' he replied, 'but it's hospital policy. You gotta go in a wheelchair.'

'Why, are they scared I might run away?' I grinned sarcastically but the joke fell on deaf ears.

I kissed Mom goodbye. She wished me luck and assured me she'd be back to visit a few hours later, during her next break. Clarendon Primary School, where she taught, was just around the corner from the hospital.

The X-ray department was below ground level and there wasn't a window in sight. A sign further down the corridor had 'Chemotherapy' printed in thick black letters. I shuddered and a heavy claustrophobia squeezed my chest. Finally Dr G arrived, looking flushed and rushed. I follow him into a small room and he made me climb onto a table covered with a cold white sheet. He was serious and businesslike and I feared this was a bad sign. A nurse joined him and they set up the room with equipment and a table of utensils. I shivered from the cold and the fear that was gripping me. The clinking noises were echoing in my head and I shut my eyes to try and block out the sound.

'Okay, Helen, please lie perfectly still,' Dr G said soothingly.

'I really don't want to do this,' I whined. 'Is it going to hurt?' I was willing him to stop.

'Just relax, Helen. It shouldn't take too long.'

Why does everyone tell you to relax when you are about to be pierced by a massive needle which you know is going to hurt?

'Keep still,' he ordered. 'I'm going to give you a local anaesthetic first.'

The thought terrified me into lying limpet-fast against the table, barely breathing. He was fiddling around, prodding parts of my back and snapping open and shut what sounded like plastic bottles. Every noise reverberated ominously in my ears. I wanted to ask what he was doing but didn't really want to know. An injection sent a sharp sting into the flesh of my back. I squeezed my eyes shut. There was a pause: the world stood still.

Then Dr G broke the silence. 'Can you feel this, Helen? Can you feel the needle?'

After a short while I could no longer feel the stinging of the needle, nor his jabbing fingers. My back was numb. I wasn't sure whether to be relieved or petrified.

'Okay, I'm going to start. Don't move,' he warned again.

I tensed every muscle in my body, readying myself for resistance. I felt mild pain and pressure deep within my back. My clammy palms gripped the table as I tried to ignore the needle poking at my loins. I felt faint from squeamishness.

'Finished yet?' I whispered.

There were a few moments of silence, then a distracted voice. 'No, I want to go in again – it looks as though I got a piece of muscle tissue, not kidney.'

He went deeper the second time and finally it was over.

In a daze I was wheeled back to the ward on a trolley and lifted onto a slightly more comfortable bed. Relief flooded through me as I realised I could finally relax. I drifted off into a hazy, exhausted sleep.

When I woke up there were four concerned faces staring down at me. It was great to see my family. How long had I been asleep? The local anaesthetic had worn off and I was now aching inside and around my back area. Dr G appeared and told us that my biopsy sample had been sent to Groote Schuur Hospital in Cape Town for specialised analysis. He explained that in the meantime I was not allowed to move for at least forty-eight hours, in order to prevent any internal bleeding.

Ugh, that means I am stuck in this ward, was my first thought. The second thought was: if I am not allowed to move, how can I go to the loo?

When I discovered my toilet would be a cold metal bedpan I stopped drinking altogether. No way did I want to wee in bed!

The night brought its own series of disruptions in the ward. A woman in the far corner of the room would not shut up. She was from the south-eastern part of South Africa and her continual moaning in the Xhosa language kept us awake. The nurses could not calm her (or they had given up trying). She had apparently been admitted for detoxification and from her actions so far she seemed half crazy too.

I eventually growled 'Shut up!', voicing the irritation of every other woman in the ward. They were all sick of listening to her shouting.

She finally drifted off to sleep some time after midnight and we were left in peace. But not for long. Soon an almighty crash broke the silence. I woke with a start and had to remind myself where I was. A couple of nurses came running with torches and we all squinted in the dark to see where the noise had come from.

Then we heard a muffled sob from the African woman and her cries began as they gathered her up, together with the broken pieces of her glass drip bottle, which she had managed to pull to the ground while trying to get out of bed. Her stilted Xhosa made it impossible to understand what she was trying to mumble. Everyone in the ward was annoyed at having been disturbed again. Eventually the nurses got the woman settled back in bed and once the drugs finally kicked in she stopped moaning and fell asleep.

This was just not the way I wanted to spend my time and I was desperate to get out of hospital. My greatest fear was that my life would never be the same again. I felt I was losing control. To maintain the power to make decisions and be in charge of my life was becoming hard. My body was failing me and I was relying on others for everything. Without my health I was powerless. Being a patient in hospital takes away your dignity so fast and you are at the mercy of the medical staff that support you when your family and friends go home. There was no time for embarrassment or concern for any of the weird procedures and tests I was going through. I was digging deep to keep my sense of humour and my strength. I had to find a route through this and ensure that I was able carry on with my life the way I wanted.

5
A New Reality

'We cannot change the cards we are dealt, just how we play the hand.'
— Randy Pausch, The Last Lecture

Most people can't bear change but I don't mind it. New experiences and a change of scenery have always been a source of excitement for me. What I realised during the days after my biopsy, however, was that my life would never be the same again. This was change on a scale like nothing I had experienced before.

One of the first big changes was to my diet. A dietician had designed a special regime to reduce the pressure on what was left of my failing kidneys. The crucial point was that it needed to be low in salt and potassium. As a young sportswoman, I had long taken an interest in nutrition but had no idea what potassium was or what foods contained it. During periods of intense sports training I would read my cereal box in the mornings and reassure myself that it had only '0.2 per cent fat'. Potassium was one of the complicated words at the bottom of the list that I ignored. Now, as my life was being turned upside down, so was the order of importance of nutritional information. Suddenly I was scrutinising all labels to see whether there was potassium, salt and protein in the contents.

The diet was the complete opposite of any I had followed before. The basic rule was that anything healthy – fruit, vegetables, meat and dairy – was bad for me (or, I should say, bad for my kidneys). This included favourites such as avocados, bananas, freshly squeezed orange juice – and chocolate. The kidneys have to remove all waste from the body. All this lovely, healthy food meant lots of waste and lots of work for my struggling organs. Certain foods contain substances that the kidneys need to clear out of the body and these just happen to be those healthy foods rich in potassium, salt and minerals that we are encouraged to eat on a regular basis. My body was full of toxins that were inadvertently being stored rather than excreted, due to the lack of kidney function. Anything I could do to reduce the amount of these toxins was worth trying.

Conversely, fat became an ally rather than an enemy. Because I needed to avoid so many foods, the only way I could get enough calories in my daily allowance was to eat fatty foods, sweets and carbohydrates. They have very little goodness in them and therefore did not stress my kidneys. It was extremely difficult to include the nine servings of fat in a day on my 'legal' list and my meals were boring, saltless, tasteless and a delightful (not!) mix of pasta, mayonnaise and sweetcorn. The only way I could eat potatoes, for example, was if they were peeled and soaked in water for twenty-four hours, to reduce their potassium content. Watching my family devour roast dinners with all the trimmings was tough. Soon, though, my appetite dwindled and food became a forced necessity rather than something to be savoured and enjoyed.

For the first time since my dieting disasters I succeeded in losing a significant amount of weight. I was soon 10 kg lighter and through no effort at all. The weight was purely excess fluid that my failing kidneys hadn't been able to excrete. By reducing my fluid intake and sticking to simple food, my body was able to stabilise. Over the coming weeks the weight continued to fall off me as I dreamt of tropical fruit salads, Avocado Ritz and melted Swiss cheese.

All this upheaval and change made me feel stressed and depressed. I avoided going out and couldn't get into the Christmas spirit. I felt extremely lethargic and found it hard to explain what was going on to anyone who asked. How could I? I barely knew myself.

When I did go out, I tried hard to act normal. I didn't appear too different, just thinner. In fact most people commented on how well I was looking now that I had lost weight. I found it interesting that looking thinner meant looking better.

I looked okay even though I was actually very far from okay. Kidney disease is often referred to as the silent killer because you really don't know that anything is wrong until it is too late. Often the indications of the disease are regular conditions like nausea, lethargy, high blood pressure and perhaps some bloating. It was hard to explain to people how sick I was or what the prognosis might be. It was easier just to say I was still trying to manage the kidney failure and we were taking it one day at a time.

As time went on I started to show signs of weakness, extreme tiredness and an aversion to food and drink. Going out with friends became even more of a struggle. Many of my friends couldn't cope with my continuing ill-health. But two who stood by me throughout were Grant, my old schoolfriend and training partner, and Jackie.

I came to rely a great deal on my dear friend Jackie, who was a real rock. She was always there for me – I never had to ask. She phoned and visited regularly to find out how I was doing, sympathised with my frustrations and tolerated my mood swings. Her empathy was unwavering and she understood heartache, having only very recently lost her mom to cancer. I was so fortunate to have her and Grant to keep my spirits up. Friends Michael, Ryan and Steve were important too. I was so grateful for their humour, their persistence and support. They all meant a great deal to me even if I wasn't able to show it at the time.

*

The biopsy results call came. I could tell it was bad as I watched Mom talking to Dr G on the phone. He wanted to see us right away, so back to Frere we went – we had hardly said goodbye to the dreadful place.

We were given the grim news that my kidney function was even worse than we had thought. I had just 10 per cent kidney function. That was all! Despite this, Dr G said he was not going to give up without a fight. And neither was I.

My diagnosis: allergic interstitial nephritis. This means the kidneys were damaged from an allergic reaction to medication and the damage was permanent. In this form of nephritis (nephrons are the filters in the kidneys – nephritis is when they are inflamed or damaged), if the medication is stopped in time, recovery is possible, but more often than not it results in chronic kidney failure.

Cause: excessive long-term use of anti-inflammatories (those damn little white pills) combined with dehydration. It is also possible that this came on top of an underlying kidney condition that we hadn't been aware of.

The renal team in Cape Town suggested steroid treatment to kick-start the kidneys and try and repair the damaged cells. It was a bit of a Hail Mary, but I didn't know that. The treatment sounded fairly simple, not that I liked the sound of *steroids*. But I was assured this was a different type of steroid to the one that body-builders use to boost their muscles.

'Just as well I am not going to be playing in the Olympics anytime soon,' I smirked. Steroids were and still are widely abhorred by sports people.

Dr G scrawled a prescription on the notepad next to him and sent a nurse down to the pharmacy. I was thinking that a few more pills wouldn't harm me, until I heard him say that I would get the drug intravenously for the first few days and only then go on to actual pills.

'I'll book a bed for you right away.' He rushed out as I was still coming to grips with this news.

'A bed? You mean I have to be admitted *again*?' I asked no one in particular. This was seriously starting to piss me off. Why couldn't I just take a few pills?

Once again everything was happening too quickly. I hadn't even brought any clothes or toiletries with me. Mom said she'd come back later with some things. I listened to the list of side effects I was going to 'enjoy', wishing Dr G hadn't bothered telling me – hunger, weight gain, a moon-face, excess hair, muscle wasting, to name just a few.

The first drip was painfully jabbed into the top of my hand and the strong liquid coursed through my veins. I felt the effects of the intravenous drug in seconds. The lights in the room seemed brighter and a vile, bitter taste developed on my tongue. As I lay in the now familiar Female Medical ward I felt a vague dread setting in. What was in store for me? Would these steroids work? I wanted this all to be over. And it hadn't really even begun!

After a few days, I left the hospital for the second time in ten days and hoped I wouldn't be back too soon. It felt good to be free of the nagging needle in my hand and I was so pleased the high dose of steroid treatment was over. The tastebuds in my mouth felt fried. Everything tasted like tinfoil and I was feeling hungry one minute, nauseous the next. Instead of the liquid steroid, I started a daily regime of swallowing thirty potent little white pills. Although still unpleasant, they were a definite improvement. I had to be weaned off the medication slowly to prevent withdrawal symptoms, reducing the number of pills every few days until I was down to zero.

News of my kidney failure was spreading fast. If I was finding it bizarre, I am sure my friends were equally stunned. Flowers and cards started arriving daily – they were so encouraging and lovely to receive. My family were overwhelmed by the kindness and support from everyone. The hardest questions were around what the prognosis was. None of us knew.

*

I had blood tests every three days at the renal clinic. The first few tests offered us all some hope. My creatinine came down from 726 to 495. A significant drop. But a few days later it shot up again and it soon became obvious that the treatment had failed.

Dr G was disappointed. I was devastated. I was so sure this kidney problem was going to be reversible. My diagnosis had gone from acute to chronic. Not good news at all. My kidney disease was here to stay.

'Dialysis' and 'transplantation' were mentioned seriously for the first time. Dialysis sounded horrendous. I could not imagine being subjected to those horrendous needles or being hooked up to a machine for four hours at a time. And the idea of a kidney transplant – well, that seemed even more outrageous. I decided it was highly unlikely I would reach the stage of needing a transplant and despite what the medical team was saying I was determined to prove them wrong. I couldn't believe this was me we were talking about.

'Are you telling me these are my *only* choices?' I asked cautiously. There had to be some other way of making me better.

Dr G was genuinely as upset as we were. He had hoped for a successful result from the steroid treatment.

We continued to discuss the preparations needed for haemodialysis. I only half listened in the hope that it might never happen. Perhaps they had got it all horribly wrong. Maybe my kidneys would start working again. What if I didn't go on dialysis – would I die? This thought made me sit up and focus my attention on his diagrams.

Dialysis was going to be the only way to keep me alive, apparently. Dr G explained that it was an artificial way of cleaning the blood and doing the job my kidneys just weren't able to do anymore. The machine that cleaned the blood did this via a series of tubes that would take my blood, wash it in a dialyser, remove waste and then return it to my body nice and clean, with the excess water removed too. The biggest concern for me was the two rather large needles that would need to be stuck into me every time in order to connect me to the tubes and the machine. One needle would remove my blood, the other would return it to me.

Regular veins are not strong enough to withstand the pressure and dialysis would break the walls of the vein. Arteries have stronger walls but they are deeper in the body. What I needed was a 'fistula' to allow a safer and stronger access point for dialysis. The operation to achieve this would join a vein to the artery in my wrist. In time, the vein would become distended by 'borrowing' pressure from the artery, allowing access for dialysis. The sooner I had the operation the better, as the fistula would take about six weeks to fully develop. It sounded as uncomfortable as everything else. I was not enjoying being a kidney patient at all.

*

Of all the operations I have had, the fistula operation was one of the worst. You are awake throughout the procedure, which is probably why I hated it so much. The local anaesthetic dulled most of the pain, but I could still feel the pulling, tugging and fiddling as my vascular surgeon, Mr Schultz, did the stitching.

It seemed to take forever. Lying on the hard metal operating table made me very cold despite the layers of heavy blankets. While he worked on my outstretched arm I tried to ask what he was doing behind the screen they had set up. I kept my eyes squeezed tightly shut to keep the pain at bay.

When at last I was wheeled into the small recovery room, I saw Mom and cried. The anaesthetic had worn off and already my wrist was throbbing. The pain continued for days and I found it difficult to sleep. I kept the wrist warm and protected in wads of cotton wool. I couldn't wear anything tight on my left wrist and started wearing my watch on the right hand. Mr Schultz said I should listen for a buzzing noise – the sound produced by blood rushing through from the artery to the vein. This would indicate that the fistula was working.

I could hear and almost feel it the first few days. I squeezed a squash ball whenever possible to strengthen the muscles and increase blood flow to the area, doing everything in my power to make sure the fistula worked.

A week later I went to have the stitches removed, nearly fainting from the experience. To my utter dismay Mr Schultz could not hear the blood-rushing sound through his stethoscope. The fistula had blocked. Reluctantly we booked another date for surgery, this time on the right arm. I would have to go through the whole torturous process again.

It was just a few days before Christmas when I finally visited the Renal Dialysis Unit on the second floor of the Frere Hospital. I had put off the visit for as long as possible, hoping that I wouldn't need to bother. Despite all the results I was being given, I was still in denial.

Sister Mac, as she was affectionately called, laid down the law loudly as soon as I walked in. She was short, buxom and Scottish and her strong accent belied the years she had lived in South Africa. 'No one is allowed to visit you while you're on dialysis,' she announced in her no-nonsense manner. 'Not even your mother. We look after you in here, young lady. Any more in this tiny ward and we will be crashing into one another.

I had very little time to say anything while Sister Mac gave me the grand tour. She knew how to talk more than me!

While she nattered on I surveyed the room and eyed a sleeping patient sitting in a corner. He had a cotton throw over him which covered the needles in his arm. But I could see the two plastic tubes carrying blood from his body. They snaked around a large computer-like machine containing a number of buttons, flashing lights and pipes coming out at the front and back. Every now and then the machine made odd beeping sounds. It looked like a lot of blood was out of his body. I wondered if he could feel anything, but was too scared to ask. A TV was playing the latest episode of the soap *Days of our Lives*.

I was introduced to another two nursing sisters – round, cheery Lulu and gentle, smiley Jenny – quite a contrast to Sister Mac. Together they made a great team and ran a good unit. However, the more I saw and heard, the more I prayed that I would not have to go onto dialysis. They said they looked forward to seeing me in the new year but I was determined to make every effort to stay away.

The festive season was interrupted by my second fistula operation. The same porter wheeled me into the operating rooms – he was surprised to see me back again. The operation went much the same as the first and despite Mr Schultz's competence and skill the second fistula, this time on my right wrist, also failed to work. He couldn't understand why they had both collapsed. My veins seemed fine.

This was becoming tiresome and concerning. I loathed having to go through the operation again – where else on my body could they try anyway? Maybe this was a sign that I wasn't meant to go on dialysis?

*

Dr G, my caring, tolerant and amazing kidney specialist, was also a lay minister at my local church. He drew great strength from his faith. It helped him cope with the challenges of kidney medicine and at a time when it was not easy to discuss issues concerning organ donation and transplantation. He spent a lot of time praying for me and at darkest moments even praying with me.

He also took the trouble to discuss how I was feeling and coping. He sensed my state of denial despite all that had I been through in the last month. At the age of twenty, I felt invincible. It was hard for me to accept that death was a real possibility. Dr G was concerned about how I would react when the realisation of the enormous changes that were taking place in my life became clearer. He really wanted me to face the facts. Did I realise that I might not play tennis again? That I might not be able to travel again? That I might not make twenty-one?

He gave me the book *Joni*, the inspirational autobiography of Joni Eareckson Tada, a young woman who became paralysed from the neck down after diving into a shallow lake. It was about how she overcame this challenge to find meaning and acceptance in her life; how her faith and immense belief in the power of prayer gave her the peace she was searching for. It was a really helpful and calming read – it made me realise that you can overcome anything. It helped fuel my fight for what I had yet to face.

I wasn't too sure about the 'God' thing though and as much as I was eternally grateful for the people around me who were praying for me every moment of the day, I was finding it hard to do the same. I had grown up in a Christian family, was encouraged (and sometimes coerced) into attending Sunday School until my competitive sport took over on Sundays, and I was taught Religious Education at school. But still I had questions. For some reason I was not convinced about faith and my belief in God. What gave people blind faith? Why was I struggling so much with this? Maybe one day it would make sense to me.

My determination to survive and get over the rather large hurdle of kidney failure in my young life was all that I was able to focus on. There was so much I still wanted to do, so much I still wanted to achieve. The plan every morning was to get through the day. Some might see this as enough of a reason to call on God's help, but my loving family, supportive friends and incredible medical team gave me all I could have hoped for to overcome my challenge.

I still didn't look unwell and on good days even I found it hard to believe that I was so seriously ill. Working out why this had happened to me was almost impossible. What lesson was I meant to take from it all? I had learnt what those two little beans did buried underneath my back muscles, but I could never have predicted the damage that could be caused from a seemingly regular medicine and a lack of water. I think the real lesson I was learning was about how fragile life can be.

Christmas Day was strained and I wished I could ease the worry that was engulfing my parents. Everyone was fussing around me and apologising for their stacked plates while I nibbled at a minuscule piece of turkey. I wasn't hungry anyway. While everyone dived and splashed in the pool I sat under the shade on a lounge chair with Mitzi on my lap. It was difficult trying to be cheery when I felt like my world was falling apart, but I was grateful to be at home with my family and not in hospital on my own. My face had swollen from the steroid treatment so I was not a pretty sight. I was hoping it would slowly reduce as I was weaned off the drugs. The hair on my head had become thicker and there was a fine layer of hair all over my body. When I eventually stopped taking the tablets in the new year, my body hair thankfully reduced and fell out. I would find it on my shirts and sheets every morning.

6
Following My Dreams

'Man cannot discover new oceans unless he has the courage to lose sight of the shore.'

– André Gide

Quite a few people reacted strongly to what we believed was the reason my kidneys had failed. I was asked regularly if we were going to sue the drug company or even the university where all this had started. We made some initial enquiries and tried to find out if this was even worth pursuing, but in Louisiana the courts follow French law and our suit could have taken years to resolve. It was not worth the time and effort while I was fighting to get well. Nor could we afford the overseas travel.

Also, the case was not cut and dried. It is possible that my kidney disease had started years before. My specialists are still not sure if perhaps I had an underlying kidney condition before I even went to America. When the kidneys are in a weakened state, any medication can cause massive damage. A full health check-up and perhaps even a blood test before I travelled might have picked this up.

Could I really blame the trainers for giving me anti-inflammatories so freely? They were treating my shin splints and tendonitis, which I desperately needed help with in order to manage the strenuous practice and frequent matches throughout the season. There was never time for rest. I was on a tennis scholarship and needed to perform to keep my spot on the team.

Should I have been more forceful during tennis practice and convinced my coach that I wasn't just trying to have a break when I needed to have a drink? Were there any warnings on the pill bottles that I hadn't seen? What about the medical profession who had let me slip through the net – the doctor in England who had detected blood and protein in my urine but done nothing about it; my family doctor in East London who took three months to diagnose my condition? Where could we begin to place the blame when in actual fact it was me who hadn't drunk enough water, me who had taken the pills and me who had ignored the ominous symptoms for months.

None of this mattered now. I couldn't put the clock back. No amount of blame or regret would change the fact that my kidneys had failed. I was a million miles away from my tennis-playing days and university life in Louisiana. I was now fighting for my life.

*

I was used to setting myself goals in all the sports I undertook. Tennis became my focus in the latter part of high school along with my favourite winter sport of field hockey. It was only when I had secured the tennis scholarship to America that tennis took over.

I had learnt that hard work, self-motivation and commitment were essential if I was to make it in my chosen sport. My parents encouraged and pushed me to train hard if I wanted to do well. I absorbed motivational books like *The Power of Positive Thinking* and autobiographies of famous athletes. I wanted to learn about and mirror their habits and skills and discover how they had turned their sport into a career. At a young age I had learnt that modelling the greats was a way of learning best practice.

The greatest gift my parents gave me was the belief that I could achieve whatever I set my mind to achieving. Mom always encouraged me to give my best. Nothing else mattered. If you won, great; if you lost but had given it all you had, then that was great too. Always, always do everything in your power to be the best you can be so that you can walk tall at the end of the day. No one could take that away from you. It gave me the confidence to expand my imagination and strive towards my goals.

I finished my final school exams in late November 1988. The next six months I set about improving my tennis as much as possible – I wanted to make a good impression when I walked onto the court in Louisiana. In addition to regular practice sessions with tennis friends, I had weekly private coaching and worked hard on my fitness. I did long-distance running, interval sprint training (I knew every lamppost on my street and exactly which houses to avoid with their monster guard-dogs), and weight- and circuit-training at the gym. I also played indoor hockey in the evenings to develop speed and fitness.

I was also working two jobs, desperately trying to make and save as much money as I could to pay for the airfare and reduce the financial burden on my parents. Although the scholarship was covering my university fees and accommodation, I would still need money for entertainment and other expenses. Chances were that I would not be able to work in the States.

During the day I worked at Taylors Sports. I had been doing so on Saturdays since I was sixteen. Most lunchtimes and evenings I was a waitress at a Swiss-style restaurant around the corner from home.

However, there was one problem that had been haunting me for some time. Shin splints. The pain had started about a year previously, making my final hockey season torturous. Pam, my hockey friend, and I had trained together for months in preparation for a week-long inter-provincial hockey tournament that winter. We were determined to make the South African team in our last year at school. As it turned out, the team I captained that year was in the B-section of the tournament and the selectors hardly gave us a second glance. It was so disappointing to be ignored and not be given a fair chance after the hours of practice we had put in. We gave it our best though and both made the South African B team to play in an exhibition match after the tournament.

I was drawing on all my strength in the final match – the pain in my legs was unbearable and all I wanted to do was lie down, curl into a ball and cry. My shins were on fire. Eventually our coach noticed that I was limping badly and called me off the pitch. I sat on the bench in tears while the team finished the tournament without me. It was the last time I was to play field hockey. I couldn't play for the rest of the season and decided to barely touch a tennis racquet until after my exams, by which time I hoped my shins would have healed sufficiently.

Captains three ... Hudson Park's Penny Hurley (left), Helen Philpott (centre) and Mandy-Lee Hobbs earned the school the unusual distinction of being named captains of their respective Border schools' hockey sides. Hurley leads the B schools team, Philpott Border A and Hobbs is captain of the Border U15 side.

Credit: East London Daily Dispatch

The best treatment anyone could recommend was ice and rest. This did not bode well if I was going to have even more intense training overseas. How was I going to manage there if the shin splints wouldn't go away? I decided to do some investigations of my own. There had to be a way of curing them. What I didn't expect was the number of doctors, specialists and therapists I would have to see to find a solution.

My first bizarre suggestion came from a friend who was a vet. She said I should try horse liniment, the same product they use on horses' shins after they have been racing. Well, I thought, it couldn't hurt, although I hoped it wouldn't make me feral. So off to the local vet I traipsed and bought a bottle of the luminescent, foul-smelling liquid. I used cotton wool to dab it all over my legs, then wrapped my legs in bandages as instructed. I lay on the couch watching television like a wounded horse. Brother Pete, my daytime-TV buddy, was disgusted with the stench emanating from my shins and soon I was dispatched to the outside veranda with a book. Even Mitzi kept away.

Apart from creating a foul smell in the house, the liniment did nothing.

I did not mention the struggles I was having with shin splints to Todd in the hope that I would be able to fix the problem before I got to Louisiana.

I was fairly good at stretching, patiently warming up before and after practice, and frozen peas were used to ice my shins after tennis to bring relief. But I couldn't survive on frozen peas and stretching alone. An orthopaedic surgeon suggested even more stretching exercises and I was referred to a podiatrist for further assessment.

The podiatrist made special moulds of my feet and then built plastic insoles which forced my feet to roll in a certain way. The supports also lifted my heels slightly to reduce the strain on my calf muscles. I waited for a reduction in the pain – no such luck. Quite frankly, all the stretching was becoming tiresome and felt like a waste of time.

Our family doctor was also brought into the debate and his opinion was that I could be losing oestrogen from all the training I was doing. It was a common problem for elite women athletes, he said. I was given a birth-control pill to replace the hormones I was supposedly losing. When I started gaining weight from the pill, I decided that this was not the way I was going to treat my shins and stopped the medication.

A runner who was a pharmacist suggested that I add a calcium supplement to my diet. He also introduced me to my first course of anti-inflammatories. I took the tablets for ten days and was advised not to over-exercise and to be alert to any adverse reactions, especially in my stomach. If at any point I felt nauseous or experienced headaches or abnormal stomach pains I was to stop them immediately. I didn't notice any side effects, but the short dose didn't help and I was back to square one.

I was becoming desperate. Nothing was having an effect and I restricted my tennis to serving hundreds of balls from the back of the court and working out at the gym.

Open to anything at this stage, I turned to acupuncture. Apparently it could help inflammatory conditions. I made an appointment with the eccentric Slovakian acupuncturist who had tried to treat my tonsils some years earlier. He hadn't managed to stop the regular bouts of tonsillitis that dogged me, especially before gymnastic competitions, so in the end I opted for a tonsillectomy. He was still upset about that. His eastern European accent made him difficult to understand, but the word 'needles' was never hard for me to identify. Have I mentioned that I am petrified of needles? In spite of his hearty insistence that we try them, I refused. Instead, I allowed him to use a laser. I was not surprised that my shins still ached after weeks of treatment. Nothing else had worked, why should this? My positive attitude was waning and I was fed up.

In a last-ditch effort to fix my legs I tried physiotherapy. My first treatment was with a very hard business-like woman who tried to convince me that the pain she was inflicting was going to help. Even though I couldn't bear to touch my legs at all for the pain, she was massaging and prodding without mercy. I survived one session with 'Iron Hands' and quickly sought another physiotherapist.

Finally I had found someone who I believed could help me – a down-to-earth, caring and experienced physiotherapist who gave me hope. She spent hours using lasers, gentle massage and ultrasound on my tender shins. Her patience and perseverance paid off. Thanks to her, along with my continued stretching and regular icing, by the time I flew overseas I was able to play a game of tennis without wincing.

The swelling and pain slowly reduced and I felt able to cope. I thought I had finally won the shin-splints battle. What I didn't realise was that this simple yet very painful condition would change my life beyond recognition.

*

Arriving in America was so exciting. It was like a dream come true. After years of aspiring to this goal, to finally get there was incredible. What hit me first was the heat. It was like walking into a humid furnace as I stepped out of the airport in Louisiana. Two of my new tennis teammates, Lauren and Tiffany, collected me from the airport. They were friendly and kind and really excited to meet me, mimicking everything I said in my foreign accent. I also found their southern drawl hard to understand at first. Within a couple of days we had become firm friends, spending hours shopping for our new life at university and enjoying the generous southern hospitality. Life in the south was relaxed. I knew I would be happy there.

The tennis team had seven girls from various parts of Louisiana and two from out of state: Kristen from Florida and me from South Africa. Kristen and I shared a room and became close friends straight away. Being the two foreigners gave us a common bond. All of us were housed on campus in the women's sports dormitory. We shared this with softballers, basketball players and athletes. It was a fun and lively environment. Meals were taken in the main sports student cafeteria with all the other athletes. There was plenty of food on offer and with the amount of training we did, we ate plenty too.

Tennis practice was every afternoon, just after lunch, and finished just before dinner. I never took the scholarship for granted and worked hard to improve and show my appreciation to Coach Todd for putting his faith in me. We trained hard and in searing heat. Just walking onto the court reduced you to a sweaty mess. The months rolled by and were filled with tennis matches and typical student fun: football games, baseball guys to hang out with (we practised next door to one another so became quite friendly) and parties on 'the strip' near the university. America was full of all the clichés I'd expected – sorority girls driving sporty TransAms, late-night drive-thrus to Taco Bell and McDonald's, music blaring out of old Chevies, people with names like Perry, Randy, Chip and Chuck, dip-spitting baseballers, footballers the size of mountains and basketballers who could reach doorposts. It was all so thrilling, the stuff of my childhood dreams.

Christmas break couldn't come fast enough. We had endured a tough first semester of studying and training. Matches brought plenty of successes and our team was faring well in the NCAA (National Collegiate Athletic Association) Division 1 competition. I was delighted with my 5-1 record after just a month of division matches. However, my dreaded shin splints had returned. The break would give the inflamed muscles in my calves the chance to heal.

Our tennis schedule for the second semester

I spent our few weeks off in Florida with friends in Orlando, including a visit to Disney World and meeting Mickey Mouse, and finished off with Kristen and her family in Cape Coral. It made the time away from my own family bearable. The Hannahs adopted me as one of their own and made me feel so welcome and cared for that Christmas. We had a time away on Captiva Island and enjoyed swims in the lukewarm Gulf of Mexico, a really idyllic spot.

When I got back to training in January the pain of my shin splints had not diminished and in fact was worse than before. I developed severe tendonitis in both Achilles and the trainers thought I probably had stress fractures in my legs. I still kept up with gym sessions, but the torture I endured when we had to jump on to four-foot-high boxes tested all my might. It was hard to rest and we were pushed to continue through the pain to keep improving and not let the team down.

Every day I now had heat treatment just before each practice session and then got my legs taped up to stop the muscles from moving. It was like walking in plaster but at least I could survive the strenuous court workouts, even if I looked stiff and clumsy. Ice baths after three hours on court were a welcome relief despite the painful first few minutes. Throughout this period, I was also managing my pain by taking anti-inflammatories – usually several tablets a day.

A few months into the new year my fitness level plateaued and I started struggling. I couldn't quite put my finger on what was wrong, apart from the pain in my shins, but I could not pull myself out of the slump I had fallen into. I got tired easily and every practice session became harder. I was also getting fatter instead of slimming down from all the training. No amount of *Slim Fast* was helping.

When our coach announced that scholarships would be halved due to a funding deficit the following year, I made the difficult decision to leave America at the end of the university year. It was very disappointing and I was sad to say goodbye to all my friends in Louisiana. I did my best to think philosophically about the change in my future direction and hoped that there was a greater plan for me.

How fast things had moved in the few short months since. I was now a kidney patient, trying to find a treatment that would keep me alive.

The USL tennis team -
we won our division that year.

7

Courage

'Healing takes courage and we all have courage, even if we have to dig a little to find it.'

– Tori Amos

I was now running out of options. With two failed attempts at creating a fistula in my wrist for dialysis, it was decided that we should seek a second opinion in Cape Town, at the world famous Groote Schuur Hospital. Cape Town is a twelve-hour drive from East London – along a really pretty coastal route – and we decided to combine the trip there with a family holiday. My medical dramas were a strain on all of us and it would be good to have a change of scene.

Michelle and Peter had been told only the basics. They must have got very frustrated when we invariably fell silent as they approached the room. I guess Mom and Dad wanted to protect them from any unnecessary worry. They were both still so young. Mich was just starting high school and at a very vulnerable age and Pete was even younger and meant to be having fun with friends, not worrying about kidney disease. When any of us went anywhere, I was always the subject of the conversation – people genuinely wanted to know how I was. It must have been very draining for my family to talk about my illness all the time, whereas at least I could hide away at home if I didn't feel like discussing it.

Groote Schuur Hospital is famous for being the site of the first successful heart transplant, performed by Dr Christiaan Barnard in 1967. It sits at the base of Table Mountain, enjoying expansive views of the city below and Table Bay in the distance. None of us was prepared for the enormity of the modern building compared to our local Frere Hospital in East London. It felt spacious and up-to-date. The walls of Hospital Street, the wide main corridor, were lined with children's art, adding a fun and lively touch.

All five of us traipsed into the Renal Unit on Level E where we were introduced to Dr Pascoe. He was direct with a dry sense of humour that took a while to get used to, but I got the impression he knew what he was talking about. His practical approach hid his empathy, but it was clear he was determined to make me well.

'I hear you are a star tennis player,' he said as he ushered us into the room.

'I guess…I was,' I replied, thinking that he must be crazy if he imagined I could still be playing tennis. I could barely walk without getting out of breath now.

'We'll have you back on the court in no time,' he quipped.

This was an interesting change in attitude from a doctor, considering the diagnosis I'd been given just weeks earlier. After a few more questions and a simple examination, he gave it to us straight. He wanted me to go on to dialysis as soon as possible and said that a transplant would be my best option for successful lifelong treatment. I felt like I had been thrown into the eye of a storm that was brewing around me and there was no way to escape. Each piece of information was making the storm bigger, stronger and seemingly impossible to break through.

In fact we should make plans for that as soon as possible,' he said.

The storm was building. He explained that I would have to go on a waiting list but that it should not take very long to find a kidney within the catchment area. I wasn't sure how long he meant, but I didn't really believe that this was going to be my future anyway so didn't bother to ask. The concept of waiting for a kidney was still so foreign to me

Dr Pascoe then went on to talk about live-related transplantation, which is when the donor kidney comes from a living relative. According to him, this was becoming increasingly popular and had met with great success around the world. It was only a matter of time before the same would be true of South Africa, he said. The key to transplantation is to prevent the body from rejecting the new organ – a natural reaction of the human body to any foreign object, be it a splinter or a kidney. When the organ donor is a close match to the recipient, there is less likelihood of rejection and a better chance of success. Live-related transplantation therefore worked well, Dr Pascoe explained, because of the closer family match.

'The success rates are slightly higher for this sort of operation,' he added.

I wanted to shout at him to hold on and stop going so fast. I was still getting my head around the possibility of dialysis, let alone anything else.

He reiterated that the risk of rejection was far less if the donor was related. However, the surgery for donors was new and it was very invasive and carried risks, like any other surgery.

Unrelated (or cadaver) donations were more common but equally challenging in that so few donors were available to the hundreds or even thousands of people waiting for kidneys and other organs. Some kidney patients waited many years on dialysis, he told us, and in fact died waiting if no match was found. This was a sobering thought.

As a family, we had not talked much about the option of a kidney transplant at this stage and I still couldn't come to grips with the idea that I might need one in the future. I had heard Mom and Dad discussing the possibility of giving me a kidney, but I was really uncomfortable with that and chose not to join in with those discussions. It made no sense to involve anyone else in the family – it was bad enough having one of us being sick

Mom then piped up that she and Dad were considering donating a kidney if they were compatible and Dr Pascoe seemed quite pleased with the idea. Were they all ganging up on me?

I decided it was time I asked some questions of my own.

'What will happen if I don't have a transplant, are there any other options?'

'Well, you could choose to survive on dialysis, but that would be your only treatment and it would be for the remainder of your life. And it would not be a long life.'

Not the answer I was hoping for. I also asked if Mom or Dad would be in any danger if they gave me a kidney. He said the risk was the same as with any operation. Great, so it could get worse!

Although,' he added, 'the chances of something going wrong are remote.' And he quoted something like a one-in-a-thousand chance of death. That one in a thousand was what I feared. I couldn't even contemplate such a disaster happening to our family.

We were introduced to Sister Evans, the transplant coordinator. She dealt with the donors and the recipients, ensuring that everything was ready for the transplant and that the correct matching procedures had been undertaken. Her warm smile put me at ease and I liked her immediately.

There was still so much to discuss and the decision about my future seemed to be out of my hands. Mom and Dad joined me in the queue to give copious amounts of blood. This was for tissue typing and cross-matching. These two vital tests would identify our blood types and check whether Mom and Dad were actually compatible with me. If their bloods had no reaction with mine, the transplant could go ahead. Once again I marvelled at the sight of so much blood leaving my body and how I was still able to get up afterwards. Sister Evans succeeded in making Michelle and Peter feel important too by giving them a tour of the unit and entertaining them with masks and other medical paraphernalia they could try on and play with while they waited.

Professor Kahn, the specialist transplant surgeon, was booked to perform my third fistula operation. What I found great about the team in Cape Town (I say 'team' because there was a large group of surgeons, specialists, registrars and nurses who worked together in the renal and transplant wards) was that they treated me like a normal, healthy person and didn't let me waste time feeling sorry for myself. From the moment I met them, their confidence gave me the confidence to believe I might actually be able to get through this – alive! We rely so much on the medical profession knowing the answers and finding solutions to our problems. When they appear knowledgeable and positive, we are more likely to believe in our ability to overcome our ill-health. During my own long-running medical drama, it was the times when the doctors looked confused, concerned or upset that I knew things were bad. They were my seriousness gauge. Conversely, in periods when I was at rock bottom, the cheery attitude of the doctors and nurses helped me stay hopeful.

I lay in a makeshift operating room which they had created that day because all the operating suites were booked up. I listened as Prof Kahn talked to the accompanying registrar about their game of tennis the night before and I was amazed at how much banter could go on during surgery while they were meant to be concentrating on my arm. I was highly stressed and nervous and tried my best to focus on his questions about my time in America. He was fascinated by sport so we had an instant connection.

He created a new fistula on my upper left arm, joining the vein and artery in the bend of my elbow. I really hoped this one would work. If it did, it might be less intrusive than the one in the wrist area. The familiar ache began soon after the anaesthetic wore off and I wanted to get home and sleep it off fast. I felt very sorry for myself as I waited for my family to return from their day out in Cape Town. Opposite me in the waiting room there was a man shackled to a ball and chain and escorted by a security guard. He must have been suffering from a kidney problem too or why would he be sitting there when he should be in jail? He made me nervous and I tried to avoid his disarming stare by skimming through a dog-eared magazine, pretending to read. It was such a relief to see Mom pop her head around the corner an hour later that I burst into pathetic 'fistulatears', as I now called them.

I wasn't able to enjoy the rest of the holiday. My cotton-woolled arm ached and throbbed constantly. While Dad took Michelle and Pete to various sights around Cape Town, Mom stayed home to care for me as I slept off the pain. I felt so guilty about spoiling the trip, but she wouldn't have it any other way. The drive home to East London was long and stressful. My elbow ached and every bump sent sharp pains through my arm, plus it was difficult to sit or lie down with three of us in the back seat.

I willed this fistula to work. Prof Kahn said he never failed so I prayed he was right. Mr Schultz had never failed either and look how his noble attempts had turned out. The next option, if this fistula failed, would be a shunt (basically a soft tube which is put in a vein) in my leg and not only would a shunt be unsightly but it would require a much larger operation. I decided three of these blasted things were enough!

The day I started to feel the buzz in my arm as the arterial blood pumped through the vein, I knew it would be okay. The vibration in my arm fascinated my friends and I learnt to live with the constant whooshing noise, which often kept me awake at night. But there was no way I was going to complain. I finally had a lifeline that worked.

*

Patience is something I don't naturally have. When I have made a decision to do something, I want to have done it yesterday. However, going through the process of coping with my new-found kidney condition was teaching me to be far more patient and tolerant about my situation. Nothing was going to happen quickly. I had to accept that my life now moved at a different pace. I was forced to take each day as it came. My goal was obviously to cope and get over it as fast as possible, but nothing about getting over kidney failure was going to be quick. Patience was going to be the only way I could handle this phase of my life.

I was still registered to begin my studies at Rhodes University in February. Peter Kirsten was ready for me to meet with him so that we could work out a sports programme for the year. I was looking forward to doing something that would take my mind off hospitals and kidneys. But I was faced with another challenge before I was allowed to begin my time at Rhodes.

It was a few days after we returned from the holiday in Cape Town that I woke up and noticed large blurry patches in my vision. I thought perhaps I had something in my eye and tried to rub out the blank spots. It progressively worsened through the day and by the time Mom came home from school I was convinced I was losing my eyesight.

Without trying to sound too alarming, I walked into the kitchen and said, 'Mom, I don't know what's wrong, but I can't see. I think I'm going blind.'

Mom, being a woman-of-action, phoned Dr G immediately, and he suggested I see an ophthalmologist.

Dr Murray, my eye doctor, bore into my eyes with his telescopes. He took numerous photos and tested my vision. I left the room feeling even more blinded from the flashes and dilating fluid than when I arrived. There was no way I could read any of the magazines in the waiting room.

He called me back inside his room a while later to give me the news. The photos of the backs of my eyes showed round yellow balls covered in red blotches.

'The blood vessels at the back of your eye have haemorrhaged. This bleeding is causing blindness and some damage to your eyes.'

That's all very interesting, I thought, but why?

He said it was caused by very high blood pressure and linked to my severe kidney failure. Then what I dreaded hearing the most came from this most unexpected source.

'The only thing that can help you regain your eyesight, Helen, is dialysis.'

Great, an eye specialist was prescribing dialysis – were all doctors in cahoots?

Dr Murray made it quite clear that no glasses, no medication and no surgical procedure would restore my vision. The only hope was that once I was on dialysis my blood pressure would be controlled and the eyes would hopefully heal themselves. There was no guarantee.

It was very frightening being told that there was nothing that a doctor could do. I had always placed so much faith in the medical profession. It gave me some idea of what it must be like to be told you have a terminal illness.

By the time I got home there was a message for me to be at the Renal Unit by eight o'clock the next morning. The wheels were in motion and I had lost all control. It only dawned on me then that my fistula was not ready. How were they going to hook me up to a machine?

8
Needle Nightmare

'You're braver than you believe, and stronger than you seem, and smarter than you think.'

– AA Milne

Mom and I were back at Frere Hospital. We trudged silently through the now familiar corridors to the Renal Unit. I left her in the small waiting room while I went in to see the team. Sister Mac had everything set up and was ordering the nurses, Lulu and Jenny, into action. Everything was blurry and I was terrified. I was desperate to have Mom there with me but Sister Mac ruled with an iron fist and I didn't have the bravado to challenge her yet.

Dr G bustled in soon after me, looking harassed. Was this a bad time? Still no one had mentioned how I was going to dialyse.

I was told on the run. 'We're going to put a catheter into your subclavian vein, near your neck.'

Oh boy, another fun little procedure to endure. The catheter would stay in place until the fistula in my arm was ready. It could be there for weeks.

'Is it going to hurt?' I asked.

'Don't worry, you will be given a local anaesthetic,' Sister Mac replied vaguely.

If I had been able to see more clearly, that would have been a good time to get the hell out of there. Instead I lay down on the bed. It was tilted so that my head was lower than the rest of my body and I briefly closed my eyes, wishing it was all over. I gratefully squeezed Jenny's proffered hand and stared at the round white light that hung from the high ceiling. The rhythmic whoosh of a nearby dialysis machine was a haunting reminder of where I was. The sounds of an action movie were coming from the TV at the far end of the room. Dr G looked very serious, dressed in a bottle-green theatre gown. He meant business and I was reminded of the biopsy a few months before.

They finally got started and I tensed at the sting of the anaesthetic. Dr G fiddled around my neck and collarbone and I felt prodding and tugging. How many needles did he need to use? How many times could you put a catheter in? He continued to prod the area while I stiffened from the tension. Time was dragging on and I wanted the procedure to be over. The torturous few minutes felt like a lifetime.

Just when I thought it was nearly over, I felt a sharp stabbing pain in my chest. I gasped in agony, only to be told to calm down, stay still and relax. Mom could hear my cries as I begged them to finish. Suddenly I found it difficult to breathe – every breath was like a knife in my chest. Was I having a heart attack? Panic engulfed me when I realised that no one was paying any attention to my cries and I might die right in front of them.

The pain increased. It was like no other I had ever experienced. Tears rolled down my cheeks and I squeezed Jenny's hand tighter as I called out for Mom.

They were getting frustrated with me. Sister Mac shouted, 'Relax, Helen!' and Dr G became tense from my persistent moaning, but I was in agony. I couldn't get enough air. The more I cried, the harder it was to breathe. At that very moment I thought: this is it, I am going to die!

'Please stop, I can't breathe!' I choked, in a last-ditch attempt to get their attention.

Finally Dr G said it was over. But the pain persisted. I was feeling faint. I heard someone mention an X-ray and they called for a hospital porter.

'I want my mom! Mom? I can't breathe!' I exclaimed hysterically.

Sister Mac gave in to my pleas and I heard Mom's soothing voice and her hand gripped mine for support.

'It hurts, Mom. I can't breathe,' I sobbed. 'Help me, please. I don't know what to do.'

She tried to relax me and told me it would be all right.

'I just want the pain to go away. *Please.*'

Where was Dr G? Couldn't he fix this? The porters finally arrived and wheeled me down to the X-ray department. Every bump and turn seared through my chest and I struggled to take short, quick breaths in an attempt to get more air.

The X-ray showed that the catheter was correctly placed in my chest and there was no explanation for my pain or breathing difficulties. I was sent back to the Renal Unit desperately unhappy and stressed. The staff were concerned and confused. The fact that I was scared of needles and had a low pain threshold made them believe I was overreacting. Dr G suspected that he might have nicked the lung, but this wasn't confirmed on the X-ray, so he was equally puzzled about my pain.

As I gulped for air like a drowning fish, my first session on haemodialysis went by in a blur.

Later that day I was admitted to the Female Medical ward, again. This time Mom demanded that they put me in a private room. She refused to leave my side and despite sitting next to me for hours, wasn't even offered a cup of tea. She used the time to mark school books while I tried to sleep. Hours later, Mom went home for supper, returning with Dad, Michelle and Peter during visiting hours. They had even managed to convince my friend Grant to join them. He hated hospitals, so I was touched that he had made the effort. Unfortunately, the timing wasn't good and the pain made it difficult to speak as I struggled to be jovial.

The sister on duty tried to tell me she knew more than the doctors and said that I needed oxygen. 'It will help you breathe.'

'Of course I need oxygen.' I scowled at her. 'The only problem is I can't bloody breathe it in!'

Dr G was worried about the persistent pain and knew something wasn't quite right. He ordered an ECG (electrocardiogram) to see if my heart was affected. It came back slightly abnormal but was nothing to worry about. He also did a blood test which showed a very low Hb (haemoglobin – red blood cells) level of 3.1 (normal is around 12). Kidney failure does reduce blood iron levels, but this was alarming. There had to be another cause. Maybe I was bleeding internally?

It was almost 11 p.m. when Dr G returned to check up on me again before going home. It was such a relief to see him and I begged him to find out what was causing my breathlessness. I was really scared. As a last resort, he stuck a syringe into my back, straight into my right lung. I had no energy left to resist yet another painful puncture and barely realised what he was doing. When he withdrew the syringe it was filled with blood. He estimated there was at least half a litre of blood inside my lung. Just as he'd suspected earlier, the catheter must have nicked the lung cavity, even though it hadn't shown up on the X-ray. That would explain the pain I had felt. There was no point in draining the blood as it would eventually be absorbed back into the body. Also, Dr G was sure the bleeding must have stopped and he was loath to inflict more pain on my already aching chest.

I was relieved that I now had an explanation for my agony, but most of all, I was upset. My concerns about starting dialysis faded into insignificance next to a punctured lung. It had been such a traumatic day. While trying to convince everyone that something was seriously wrong, I had been made to feel like a performing child. After all my failed fistulas, my fading eyesight and now this totally unnecessary pain, I was sensing that nothing in my medical journey was going to be straightforward.

Something still had to be done about my low haemoglobin. Dr G called the Cape Town team in the morning to see if they would send some EPO (erythropoietin) for me. He was told only patients at Groote Schuur Hospital were allowed the 'liquid gold'. It was hugely expensive and I would need at least two or three injections a week. The pharmacy at Groote Schuur said they only made allocations three or four times a year to patients in need of the drug – and I was not one of them. Even when Dad offered to pay, they refused to help.

Because my kidneys weren't functioning, there was no way I could build up my red blood cells without intervention. There was no choice: I had to have a blood transfusion. We had tried to avoid this due to the risk of antibody build-up in potential transplant patients. If the plan was to put me forward for transplantation then the fewer antibodies the better. The more antibodies I developed, the greater the chance that I would reject a new kidney. The other risk around blood transfusions was contracting hepatitis or even HIV, which is why literally keeping it in the family was a better option. He took the blood from Mom.

I went home a few days later with a still soaring creatinine of 1099 and an Hb of 6 – which was better than 3 but nowhere close to normal. My tiredness was now even more extreme and I had no energy or strength. I was beginning to walk like an old person and felt frail. My fitness was a distant memory and my muscles had started to waste away. I was positively skinny.

*

The catheter was now part of me, protruding from my collarbone. Bras were no longer an option because the straps were in direct contact with the wound. I was very conscious of the plastic tube and nervous that friends would bump into me or touch it by mistake. It made me realise how often physical contact is taken for granted. It was the middle of summer and I couldn't swim or enjoy the beach with my friends.

Fortunately, the breathing became easier as the puncture to my lung healed. When friends asked me how I was, I still didn't know how to answer. Despite feeling okay at times and feeling a little better once I had started my dialysis, I was struggling to be normal. I tried to avoid fuss and to just get on with things. However, my four hours on the dialysis machine three times a week were a constant reminder of my kidney failure. Nobody was allowed in the Renal Unit and none of my friends had ever seen a dialysis machine. It was hard for them to imagine and hard for them to understand what I was going through.

My eyesight took a couple of months to return to almost normal. I still had blind spots and it looked like I was always going to have them. However, it was so exciting to be able to read and enjoy TV again. I was no longer scared of going blind.

Those first few weeks of dialysis went by quickly. I just went through the motions: up early on dialysis days, drive to the hospital, sit on the machine, home after five hours to sleep off the dialysis headache, up for a light dinner in the evening, enjoy a day of normality before it all started again. February arrived and with it the new university term. Despite my new routine, I was determined to begin my Business Commerce degree at Rhodes University.

In less than three months, I had lost more that 15 kg but everyone continued to think I was looking quite well. Most of my fellow students had no idea I had no kidney function. I attended early-morning lectures at 7.30 a.m. for an hour before heading over to the Renal Unit on dialysis days. After dialysis and a sleep, I returned for evening sessions. Lectures were offered twice a day, morning and evening, to accommodate part-time students with jobs.

I knew I should be grateful that there was a treatment for kidney failure but dialysis was such a tedious process. It was draining and extremely time-consuming. While my friends were studying, working or having fun, I was hooked up to a machine, either battling a whopping headache or vomiting while my blood pressure plummeted.

Mondays were the worst. Having the weekend between treatments meant two days in a row without dialysis. During the week I dialysed every other day. Being 'overloaded' was really unpleasant. I became breathless and felt heavy and swollen, as if there was water in every cell of my body which my poor failing kidneys had not been able to remove. Even the knuckles in my fingers became invisible on bad days. My legs swelled up from the fluid retention and I had bags under my eyes.

My family knew that I needed sleep on Mondays. They were helpless and did their best to leave me alone. Lying in the dark, I squeezed my temples for hours to massage the painful dialysis headache away. I usually emerged from my room at around 8 p.m. to have a snack. I normally missed lectures on Monday nights so my friend Michael took notes for me. Commercial Law was dull anyway; with a headache it was even worse.

The Border Kidney Association kindly paid for a videotape contract (DVDs were still a thing of the future at that time). This allowed me and my fellow patients to enjoy two videos a week while we were dialysing. I also tried to do my assignments when I felt up to it or slept to make the time go faster.

Dialysis was the fastest weight-loss programme I knew. I would weigh in at 53 kg and walk off the machine weighing 50 kg. Three kilograms in four hours – no diet could beat that! The machine removed up to three litres of fluid from my blood during each session. A healthy person urinates and sweats out about that amount in two days. I was hardly weeing at all and for the first time ever, I was sleeping through the night without needing the toilet. Sometimes I would sit on the loo for fun, remembering what it was like to wee.

The diet I was put on to preserve my remaining kidney function was relaxed a little. Although I didn't have to weigh my food, I had to stick to the rules: no salt, no potassium, no protein and only 750 ml of liquid a day (which wasn't much during the heat of the South African summer). I sucked ice-cubes and sipped small amounts all day. I became known as the 'half-a-glass girl' because I left half-drunk drinks all over the place. Food with a high water content like cucumbers and fruit had to be limited too. I thought I would crave all the things that I was denied, especially chocolate, avocados, oranges and bananas, but, surprisingly, the damage these potassium-rich foods could wreak on my heart put the fear of death into me and quashed any urges that arose. There was a small window while you were on the machine when you were allowed to eat forbidden foods but I normally felt so nauseous that I couldn't stomach anything exciting anyway.

A small mercy in the first six weeks on dialysis was the presence of the subclavian catheter that had previously caused me so much pain. The tubes from the dialysis machine were connected straight onto the catheter, which meant no needles for the time being. Too soon, though, Dr G decided that my fistula was strong enough to be used. I would now be forced to endure those horrible needles the size of a drinking straw that were the usual way of hooking a patient up to the machine – and not just one but two of them!

When Lulu pulled out the 20-cm-long catheter tube from my subclavian I felt like I was losing a close friend. 'No wonder that damn thing pierced my lung!' I exclaimed when she showed me how long it was.

Lulu and Jenny were the only two nurses who were game enough to needle me. And they were great at it. After the catheter debacle, Sister Mac could not face my complaining and left the job to them.

When Lulu and Jenny were on leave, it was very stressful for all of us, so they made every effort to be there on the days I dialysed. They later told me how nervous I made them feel as each time I begged them not to hurt me and prayed they wouldn't miss the vein.

I began to hate dialysis even more with the dreaded 'straws'. I never got used to them. They hurt. Over time the pain diminished because of the repetitive process and development of scar tissue on my fistula. It was only many years later that I discovered that most patients are given numbing cream before the needles are put in. There was no such thing for me.

There were normally four to five patients in the unit, mostly women, and we all dialysed on Mondays, Wednesdays and Fridays. On the odd occasion we had a visiting patient or an acute patient who needed just one or two sessions. The others had been dialysing for many years and hardly uttered a complaint. It was a sobering realisation: without a transplant, I too would be on dialysis for the rest of my life. One of them was an elderly lady whose skin was greyish and shrivelled. Over the course of her lifetime she'd received over two hundred blood transfusions, which meant the doctors were not able to offer her a transplant. She had developed too many antibodies.

'You're young, Helen. You will do well with a transplant,' she told me.

I was still not sure, but anything would be better than dialysis – it had to be. I could not do this for the rest of my life.

We didn't talk much and I gleaned most of the information about my fellow kidney patients from the nursing staff. One morning the elderly lady didn't turn up. Her seat was moved to the back and the machine lay silent. She had died during the night

I was so grateful to be looked after by such caring nurses. Lulu, Jenny and Sister Mac put up with my moods, shared in my joys and gave me hugs whenever things went from bad to worse. They formed part of my growing new kidney family.

As I continued treatment on dialysis, what Nelson Mandela said about fear really rang true for me: 'I learnt that courage was not the absence of fear, but the triumph over it. The brave man is not he who does not feel afraid, but he who conquers that fear.'

9
In Limbo

One day at a time –this is enough.
Do not look back and grieve over the past, for it is gone;
and do not be troubled about the future, for it has not yet come.
Live in the present and make it so beautiful that it will be worth
remembering.

– Ida Scott Taylor

I settled into a routine, juggling dialysis with my part-time studying at Rhodes University and working at Taylors Sports when Dad needed me. I was in limbo, waiting for a kidney donor, but I was coping.

The nurses at the Frere had placed a poem on the Renal Unit wall called 'One day at a time' and they decided that it should be my guide to living during this period. I learnt not to make long-term plans; even a prearranged barbeque was hard to commit to because I often woke up feeling awful or had to go into hospital for some complication that had popped up. I was advised to hold off planning holidays or trips away as I needed to be in constant contact with the renal team in case a kidney became available. Every time the phone rang, especially late in the evening, we would have a moment of panic before we heard who was on the line. We were all waiting. My life was on hold while dialysis kept me alive.

We had been told that Mom's kidney was a potentially good match and she was eager to undergo further testing. I was still very unsure about her being my donor and was not particularly supportive of the idea. But I realised that it was an option that could not be ignored. I did not want to spend the rest of my life on dialysis.

If we went ahead, we decided it would have to take place in the June/July school holidays. That way, Mom wouldn't miss too much school. I vaguely listened to the plans but doubted they would come to fruition. However, Mom continued with preparations. She bravely went through ultrasounds, scans and X-rays and faced the rigorous tests with no complaints and the determination she always shows.

In the meantime I was top priority on the organ-donor waiting list that was held at Groote Schuur Hospital, but the real issues surrounding organ donation and transplantation hadn't dawned on me. I still didn't believe I would actually have a kidney transplant. We were told to stay close to the phone, keep calls short so that the line was clear and be ready at a moment's notice. When a kidney became available, they would call me. Timing would be critical.

When we finally did received the call from Dr G late one Saturday night in April, it was such a surprise. There was a possible kidney for me. What a strange mix of emotions: elation at the hope of getting off dialysis and sadness knowing that someone had died to make this happen.

'Get some rest. I'll call you when everything is arranged and the tissue typing is confirmed,' he said, and hurriedly hung up. How were we meant to sleep after hearing that?

I did not have long to contemplate my fate. My hopes were dashed the following morning when Dr G called to say that it was a false alarm and the organ wasn't suitable.

Such deflation! I had come so close to being freed from dialysis and needles. It made me realise that I did want a new kidney and I could only hope that one would become available soon.

*

And so my limbo-life continued. A sports committee had been chosen at Rhodes University and along with Peter Kirsten we were to develop the sports curriculum at the small campus. I coordinated the development of tennis and women's hockey. My friend Grant became team coach and for the first time Rhodes University, East London entered a tennis team in the league, albeit not at the top. I managed to find a coach for the newly formed hockey team and took on the role of manager. The team began that winter in the local league and the girls were enthusiastic and determined to have a good season. So, despite feeling dreadful most days and having to face those vile needles three times a week, I was leading a fairly full life. Many of my friends were under the impression that my illness was under control. Much to my relief, it had at least slipped into the background.

Grant had become one of my closest friends. He spent many hours keeping me company and I hope that I gave him the friendship he needed then too. We had a complicated relationship at a time when I really wasn't able to give much to other people. My battle to survive was all-encompassing. My feelings towards him were mixed. Sometimes he made me feel so special; at other times I wondered if he just felt sorry for me. I desperately wanted to be normal, look normal and feel normal. All my friends were enjoying relationships – not me. Who would be attracted to a girl with no kidneys and a buzzing arm who was on dialysis three times a week and spending most of her spare time in hospital? The uncertainty and complications would be too much to bear.

I realised that I would not be the most exciting girlfriend, but Grant was the closest friend I had and the nearest thing to a boyfriend at the time. I really valued our many afternoons drinking tea and eating toast on the veranda. However, sometimes I felt he was more relaxed around the rest of the family than with me. Then again, they weren't sick.

Dieter, a friend of Grant's from school, had also become one of mine. He was a tremendous support, although I am sure he didn't realise this. His wisecracking sense of humour helped me to forget my illness and we enjoyed great conversations at times when I really needed them.

Both Dieter and Grant forgave my mood swings, understood my tiredness and accepted my strange treatments and procedures. I was always grateful for the way they never gave up on me. I must have been the worst friend ever, yet they included me in everything. I did my best to appear normal and convince them that I was coping so they wouldn't feel uncomfortable or stop inviting me out. Together with Jackie and some of my wonderful old school friends, they kept me cheerful. I really couldn't have managed without these friends. They were amazing.

Not everyone knew what to do or how to support us. Some were better at it than others. Wherever I went there was the elephant in the room that was my kidney failure. It fascinated me how people would ask my family how I was doing but often avoided the question when they saw me. They even went so far as to ask Mom how I was when I was standing right next to her.

'You can ask Helen yourself, she is right here.'

It was as if being ill meant you were less of a person. Or maybe they just didn't want to upset me or didn't know what to say?

I was disappointed in some friends who avoided me. Perhaps they'd got bored of the ongoing saga of my condition or perhaps they simply didn't care. I remember one of them saying that they felt really uncomfortable when they visited me and didn't know what to say. They felt guilty if they talked about all the fun they were having – being twenty years old, they were enjoying life to the full – and yet they didn't want to ask me too much about my illness, so they were stuck for things to say. Little did they realise how much I enjoyed hearing about their adventures. Although I envied their fun, I also loved the distraction of their stories and the entertainment factor.

Losing touch with friends is natural and maybe this would have happened anyway, but I think my kidney failure provided a catalyst for solidifying some friendships and ending others prematurely. People surprise you when you least expect it. Anyone who has been seriously ill will understand what I mean.

During this period I spent more time with my parents' friends than with people my age. They seemed better able to handle my situation. Joan and Gordon in particular were a huge support to us. We have been close friends for as long as I can remember and Joan always made herself available for visits, to give lifts, even taking me shopping or out to tea.

Michele was another kind long-standing family friend. While the family were at work or school and my friends were too busy to visit or not brave enough to take me out, Michele would arrive and drag me out to coffee shops and tea rooms all over East London. We would go shopping together and sometimes I would spend time at her beautiful home.

The support we got from friends and family both in our community and across South Africa was incredible. We learnt that every minute of every day someone was praying for me and my family. We also had fantastic meals delivered on a regular basis by a variety of people who knew how difficult it was for Mom and Dad to plan a normal life around my impromptu hospital visits. It was strange at first and we all felt a little embarrassed that friends felt they needed to give us food. Then we realised that this was their way of helping and showing they cared. Everyone needs to be able to help in their own way. Once we had understood this, it was easier to accept their very generous help and not feel so embarrassed. Thelma, our loyal live-in maid, even began to wonder if her job was in jeopardy. She was normally chief chef, but if Mom didn't have time to shop, the 'meals on wheels' were a welcome arrival of an evening. It was always exciting opening the dishes to find out what we were being treated to.

The Clarendon Schools (a group of all-girls schools in East London), in particular Clarendon Primary, where Mom was now headmistress, also gave us incredible support. The pupils, their parents and all the staff were caring and understanding – they certainly lived up to the school motto, 'Clarendon Cares'.

Another extraordinary development was that friends and business contacts of my parents from all over South Africa got together to establish a special fund in my name. The expenses related to my illness were already huge and were becoming even more colossal. We had used up our private health insurance allowance within the first few months of my diagnosis and over the coming years would have to finance countless flights to Cape Town for both myself and my family and pay for special medication, emergency procedures and even food.

When we first heard about it, the fund had already reached thousands of rand – the equivalent of thousands of pounds. Nolan, our friend and lawyer, was tasked with managing it. The thoughtfulness and generosity of the contributors was beyond our wildest imagination. No one wanted thanks, many wanted to remain anonymous, but all donors wanted to help in whatever way they could to ease the stress and suffering and make our challenging time a bit easier. It was both humbling and overwhelming to experience this sort of support.

I didn't feel that I deserved all this generosity and kindness. But I was so grateful to everyone and really appreciated the boost that my parents and siblings were getting as a result of this fund. It was up to me to decide how it was spent and in the months and years that followed I didn't hesitate to draw on it for any expense that related to my illness. Flights were covered. Food while I was in hospital was covered. Travel for Mom and Dad to visit me was possible, which helped keep my spirits up and gave me the vital support I needed to cope. Equipment and everyday purchases were bought with less stress.

Even at this uncertain stage in my kidney drama, I was well aware that the only way to truly thank everyone who had been so generous with their time, money and support was to make the most of every opportunity I was given and keep fighting.

10
A Second Chance

'Sometimes life gives you a second chance because just maybe the first time you weren't ready.'

– Anon

The fateful call finally came one Sunday morning in late May. I was watching the women's hockey team that I managed when I saw my friend Clair running down the slope towards the field, waving her hands.

'Helen,' she puffed, 'your Mom says you need to get home right away. She just phoned our house and said to come and get you. She said you had to hurry.'

A million thoughts spun around in my head but I dared not entertain the possibility of another kidney in case I was let down again. This was before the age of mobile phones – we may as well have been using smoke signals.

As I approached the house, Mom was pacing the pavement. Her concern was masked with excitement.

'Helly Bells, quick! The Transplant Unit called a little while ago and they want you to fly to Cape Town. Today!' She hardly took a breath. 'They've found a kidney for you.'

We both raced indoors and wondered what to do next. Mom kept looking out the lounge window hoping Dad would arrive back from the middle of his tennis tournament. Luckily he hadn't been on court.

Just then the phone rang. Mom ran to answer it. I sat on the chair and stared ahead of me. I felt strangely calm as the pandemonium continued around me. This was *the one* – I knew it. Dad screeched into the driveway and wanted to know the latest news. Mom came off the phone and said that Dr G was on his way down from church.

A few minutes later he walked business-like into the lounge and we had a family conference.

'Helen, you need to decide whether or not you want this kidney.'

I felt a heavy weight descend on my shoulders. Why did I have to make that decision? Surely I should take the kidney? Wasn't this what we had all been hoping and praying for? I hadn't realised I had a choice.

'Your mother is due to give you a kidney in a few weeks' time. Hers will almost surely be a better match. However, that does not mean this one won't work,' Dr G continued gravely.

We had half an hour to make up our minds or they would give the organ to someone else. This was a difficult decision, not made any easier by the pressure of time. I was determining my own destiny. The weight got heavier.

'I've told you the risks of transplantation. You could reject this one, but then you could reject your mom's as well. There are no guarantees.'

Was there any point in going through the trauma of surgery if the chances of success were so slim?

'On the other hand,' he continued, 'if this kidney works, it will save your mom from surgery.'

That was it – decision made. I was taking the kidney. Why put Mom through undue stress and pain when I had a kidney waiting for me right now? I really did not want her to suffer and Dr Pascoe's 'one-in-a-thousand' statistic rang in my ears as I recalled the worst possible scenario.

'Are you sure, Helen? I am still ready to give you a kidney, my darling.' Mom was concerned that I was being too hasty.

'I'm not sure, but I think we should go for it.'

Dr G hurried to the phone and arrangements were made. Mom and I started rifling through my wardrobe in an attempt to pack a few things. I would have to fly to Cape Town alone and Mom and Dad would drive down the next day, all being well. Dad raced back to the courts to play his next match, although I have no idea how he concentrated on the game. In the meantime, Dr G went to the hospital to arrange the paperwork, book flights and pack the blood samples from the donor that I would have to take with me. The donor organs had already been flown to Cape Town on an earlier flight. We went to the airport via the hospital to collect everything

I stared at the little paper-covered box of blood samples and said a silent prayer for this stranger who had died and whose family was generous enough to allow the organs to be used for transplantation. How I hoped this would work. Dr G hugged me and wished me well.

Mom and I then stopped off at the tennis courts to say goodbye to Dad. By now everyone had heard about the kidney. It felt strange walking past friends as they wished me luck. What they were thinking? Transplantation was still a relatively new treatment for organ failure and now I was about to undergo this life-saving procedure. We spotted Dad on a far court and he jogged off without hesitation.

I didn't know what to say. Would I see him again? What if something went wrong and I didn't make it? There was so much I still wanted to do and say. It was too frightening to think about and I cried in Dad's arms as he hugged me goodbye.

I felt fear, sadness and apprehension. I tried to memorise every moment as if it were my last. Mom and I left with the players waving good luck and shouting their best wishes.

Mom wanted to fly down with me and I wanted that too. However, I would be going straight into theatre and would only wake up late on Monday. It would be better for her and Dad to drive to Cape Town on Monday morning.

I felt very alone and fragile as I sank into the large business class seat – there had been no other seats on the plane. Ironically I couldn't even enjoy the food as I had to be nil-by-mouth until surgery.

As I rested my forehead against the window, I thought about the donor and their grieving family. Who had died? What was their family feeling? How were they coping with the knowledge that someone like me was getting their loved one's kidney? It was difficult to feel elation about my transplant when I knew that someone had died in presumably tragic circumstances. Their organs were going to save my life and those of four other people who were also waiting for a second chance. This was the bitter irony of transplantation.

Gazing blindly at the coastline thousands of metres below, snapshots from my life filled my head: as a child swinging under the guava tree in our garden and laughing when the wind grabbed my hair; hearing the waves crashing on the rocks as I climbed the mountain at Hole-in-the-Wall; feeling the arms of my friends around my shoulders as we sang our final school song; breathing the claustrophobic heat of the Louisiana air; enjoying one of Dad's famous *braais* in the garden with family and friends. I thought of my beloved animals, Mitzi and Gabby my new little Jack Russell and Kitty, and wondered if they understood what was happening.

My thoughts drifted from the past to the future. What about all the things that I hadn't done yet? Would I ever get a chance to fulfil my dreams? I was not ready to die. This operation had to work. I wanted to live!

*

Twenty minutes after exiting Cape Town's airport, I took a deep breath, gently lifted the box of bloods and walked determinedly through the glass doors of Groote Schuur Hospital.

When I approached the admissions counter I didn't know what to say, so I tried, 'Hi, I am Helen Philpott. I've just flown in from East London to have a kidney transplant.'

All I got was a cursory nod from the woman before an abrupt, 'Take a seat.'

'Are you sure? I don't think I have time to "take a seat".'

But the woman had already turned her back. I sat hesitantly on a chair near the counter. After ten minutes I returned to the counter and rang the bell.

'I'm sorry to bother you, but I'm supposed to have a kidney transplant and the operation is very time-sensitive. I need to get to the Transplant Unit right away.'

Before she could answer, I heard, 'Miss Philpott, window two please!'

After spelling my name three times to a disinterested clerk and watching my life-history being typed one finger at a time, I was finally allowed to enter the hospital corridor. Fortunately I knew where to go; no one had offered to escort me.

The transplant team was frantically running around the unit when I rang the bell to announce my arrival. They wanted to know what had taken me so long and were astounded that I had been asked to fill in admittance forms. A nurse dressed head to foot in green bustled me into a sterile but bright private room opposite the kitchen. The sun was streaming through the double-glazing and I could see Table Bay glistening in the distance. A lone sparrow was perched on the outside ledge. It flew away as the green-clad nurse neared the window to turn the blinds. I lifted my case on to the chair and wondered what I was supposed to do next.

The Renal Transplant Unit is an isolated ward and only authorised personnel can enter. Visitors need to cover their clothes in green surgical gowns, booties and caps in order to prevent infections being transmitted.

'You must shave, lovey, and I will get you a theatre gown to wear,' said the nurse whose name had already escaped me. Shave?

'Do you want me to help you or can you manage?' she asked as she started for the door.

'I think I can manage,' I said before I realised where I had to shave and how big a job it actually was.

On the other side of the bed was a chest of plastic drawers, which on closer inspection I discovered was filled with all sorts of medical contraptions ranging from plasters and bandages to syringes and blood tubes. There was a telephone resting temptingly on top. A basin and mirror were on a wall near the door and a large white board opposite the bed had 'Helen Philpott – East London' scribbled in black along the top.

The nurse returned and started counting my possessions. She asked if I had any valuables for the safe.

'You can't be too careful, even in an isolated ward, I tell you,' she blabbered.

I was given two razors, a towel and a starched hospital gown and was instructed to shave from my belly button to my knees. I reluctantly walked to the shower for the dreaded task. Once I began shaving, I realised why she had given me two razors. Hairs were falling en masse and matting up the blades. In the midst of this hairy operation, I heard a knock at the shower door and the nurse called out to see if I was okay.

'Fine!' I shouted and tried to speed up. The drain was clogging up! I stepped out feeling like a plucked chicken and apologised for the mess in the shower as I passed the nurse. 'I didn't realise I had so much hair.'

She laughed then and told me it was okay, everyone was shocked the first time they shaved 'down there'.

The anaesthetist came to see me. He prescribed a pre-med to relax me and raced off saying he would see me in theatre soon. Another young girl from Cape Town was receiving the donor's other kidney and she was already undergoing her operation. Unlike me, she hadn't had far to travel.

It didn't take long for the pre-med to take effect. I dozed off peacefully until I was woken by a man with a big grin and a jovial woman from the surgical team who had come to collect me. The ward staff wished me good luck and said they would see me soon. I hoped so. The happy duo steered me through a maze of corridors and stopped outside the theatre. A sudden chill swept over me and I started to shiver. I wasn't ready for this.

Another nurse started fiddling with my arm and jabbed a drip painfully into my right hand. It was so quick I had little chance to complain. She told me that the other young woman's transplant had gone well, which gave me hope.

Soon it was my turn to be wheeled into theatre. They transferred me to a hard cold metal operating table. I shivered uncontrollably.

The anaesthetist entered the room and behind him came Prof Kahn and a few other doctors I didn't recognise. They all seemed in fine spirits as they greeted me and asked me how the flight had been.

'Good, thanks. First time in business class, but such a bugger that I couldn't enjoy the food and wine,' I joked back.

I felt my arm being tightened by the blood-pressure cuff. The enormous lights above looked like bright flying saucers. They reminded me of being in a dentist's chair but I was a long way away from a dentist's now. Through the monitor I heard my heart. It was beating with surprising regularity.

I wanted to ask if I was going to feel anything but decided that was a stupid question. These doctors were going to cut me open and put a foreign kidney inside me. Would I feel it? Would it work? I was scared. In fact, I was petrified. Suddenly a million questions entered my mind and I wanted to stop the clock.

The last thing I remembered was the anaesthetist saying, 'Okay, Helen, I'm going to begin to administer the anaesthetic now. Sweet dreams. Think happy thoughts.'

So soon? Wait…

*

I faded in and out of my deep slumber. The operation was over. I was back in my room in the Transplant Ward. The nurses floated like green angels as they moved around the dimly lit room. They kept measuring something near my neck, apparently checking the levels of medication in my blood. They adjusted monitors, checked the drips and kept me comfortable. There were many tubes and drains attached to my body. I didn't want to move in case something hurt. I was strangely numb and feeling still and stiff.

After a few hours I wriggled my fingers and gingerly tried to move my legs under the heavy blankets. There was no pain. I just felt sleepy and numb. The oxygen mask was irritating me and I wanted to pull it off, but a green-gowned angel with her hair pulled back tightly underneath her cap said I needed it a bit longer. I tried to relax and breathe in the cool air.

*

Sister Pam woke me up early on Monday morning. My dreamlike state was over. More observations and blood tests were performed and even though I felt like I could sleep for another twelve hours I was forced to get up.

'Good morning, madam,' she said in a playful tone. 'How are you feeling with your new kidney?'

That's right, I thought, I have a new kidney. No more dialysis! The realisation made me want to jump up and dance and sing to the world, but all I could manage was a mumbled, 'Great, I think?' I hadn't had a chance to do much more than wake up.

'Soon you will be up and about, but I think we might give you a bit of time to recover today.'

Thank heavens for that! The thought of moving was not high on my list of priorities. I was petrified of the pain that I was sure would be there if I stood up. I tried to lift my legs a little and the stabbing sensation that shot through the muscles of my abdomen was enough to keep me moulded to the bed.

At 9.30 a.m. a team of medics ranging from urologists and nephrologists (kidney specialists) to surgeons, nurses and transplant coordinators entered the ward. About fifteen people crowded into my little room. They all wore green gowns, green booties, masks and caps and *all* eyes were on me.

Prof Kahn spoke first. 'Great, I see you have been sent chocolates already. Well, we can eat those – *you* shouldn't! How are you feeling?'

I didn't have much time to respond while they spoke amongst themselves for a while and discussed my figures and blood results. The operation had been a success. One of the doctors checked my blood pressure and then prodded my abdomen. The plaster to the side of my tummy was enormous. There was a blood-filled tube escaping from beneath the plaster – I wasn't looking forward to having that taken out.

Wee was always a prominent subject in a kidney ward. I was producing a good amount, apparently.

'Looks like your new kidney is performing well already, 'said one of the consultant physicians, Professor Swanepoel. 'Make sure you drink regularly, even if it is just little sips throughout the day.'

'You mean no more restrictions?' This was exciting. 'Am I allowed to eat everything now too?' I asked.

'Not just yet, Helen, but soon, definitely. Give your body time to recover and give your kidney time to start doing its job. See you tomorrow and keep up the good work.'

There was a mass exodus as they moved on to the patient next door. The room felt decidedly quiet and I missed their banter already.

My morning routine started in earnest the next day: blood pressure and temperature checks at 5.30 a.m., morning tea, weigh-in, washed and dressed, all by 7 a.m. This was not my idea of fun and I struggled to keep a pleasant manner, barely managing a friendly 'Good morning' at such a ridiculous hour of the day.

Soon after all the activity, though, I was back in bed and drifted off to sleep amidst the clinking of medical bottles, the vacuum cleaner down the corridor and the general chatter of the staff. Nurses did not believe in keeping their voices down on any wards.

I dreamt of the outside world. I was strolling down a deserted beach with my toes sinking into the warm sand and the waves lapping over my feet. I reached a rock at the far end and sat alone, gazing out to the endless waves crashing into shore. The image changed and I was in the countryside sitting on top of a large mountain overlooking valleys and plains. The sky was crisp but the sun was warm on my skin. Finally I moved from the mountain to the garden at home and I could hear the children next door playing cricket. A ball flew over the wall and landed in the pool – splash.

*

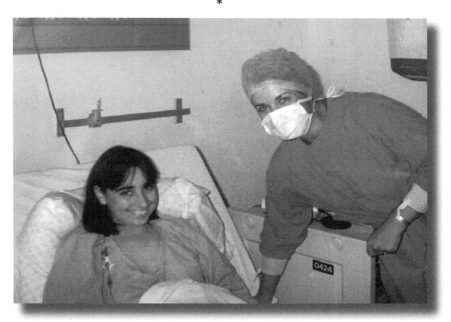

That's Mom behind the mask and me soon after the first transplant.

During my three weeks on the Transplant Ward I became known as Lady Di – everyone thought I was treated like a princess by my friends and family. This was because I was showered with cards, gifts, phone calls and even visitors, despite being a day's drive from my home town. Mom and Dad made sure that everyone rallied round and supported me whenever they had to go back to East London to work. The staff were kind and tried hard to make me feel comfortable and cared for even though I was so far from home. Most of the other patients were from Cape Town or at least the Western Cape area so they had more visitors. I was one of the few English-speaking people in the ward. The rest of them were Afrikaans or spoke a traditional African language.

I was on three types of immunosuppressive drugs: prednisone, cyclosporin and azathioprine. Immunosuppressants are aptly named – they are designed to literally suppress (or stop) the body's in-built immune system from doing its job and fighting any alien intruders, including a transplanted organ. My immunosuppressants worked together to block any rejection and convince my body that the new kidney belonged to me and should not be attacked. The concoction of pills I took each morning and night was quite something. It took me ages to swallow nearly twenty pills with twenty sips. One evening I saw another patient swallowing all twenty together and decided to give it a go. I immediately realised how much easier that was and soon was throwing them down my throat with one slug of water. This was a great achievement for someone who previously would chop paracetamol into little pieces before swallowing a single dose. I also had to swill special medication for my mouth and gums to prevent ulcers.

I was warned of the many side effects that could develop from the drugs. Every morning I scrutinised my face in the mirror for signs of hair and puffy cheeks. It was going to be difficult to fight off the side effects, but I was determined to try. I watched what I ate and even though I was allowed chocolate and other delicious previously banned foods once more, I restricted myself. I actually lost weight in the first few days. This wasn't difficult as the hospital food was terrible. If it hadn't been for my parents and friends I wouldn't have eaten at all. They bought me ready-made meals and salads from

Woolworths to keep me eating. Dad would be most disappointed when I only managed a few mouthfuls, but those mouthfuls were blissful compared to the three-day-old stews and dry bread that the Groote Schuur kitchen served. It even beat the dinner of steak-and-kidney pie we were offered the day after my transplant – talk about ironic. I starved that night!

Daily blood tests kept track of my kidney function, signs of rejection and the medication levels in my blood. Too much of my immunosuppressive medication would be toxic to both the kidney and other organs; too little could spark rejection.

My blood pressure, temperature and urine were measured and checked every two hours. I was constantly asked how much I had been drinking and was encouraged to finish the jug of water next to my bed as well as the numerous cups of tea we were served throughout the day. This was hard after the months of being on fluid restrictions while on dialysis. Sometimes it felt like I was swallowing sand as my stomach would constrict with nerves at the thought of drinking so much. But it was also so good to be able to quench my thirst.

All transplant recipients were encouraged to ride the bicycles in the television room. Once my catheter was removed, I was keen to pedal. Every minute I cycled in front of the TV, the stronger I became.

All patients in the Transplant Unit at Groote Schuur were given special attention, and that included access to a telephone. You couldn't call out on the phone, but anyone could call in. And mine rang a lot! Sister Pam sometimes took it off the hook to make sure I rested during the day.

Phone calls brought some welcome normality to the dreary hospital routine and after a while they brought a bit of excitement too. My story had reached the newspapers and people who had not known about the potentially serious side effects of anti-inflammatories were shocked to discover what had happened to me. I received calls from members of the public who got through via the switchboard and wanted my advice. They would ask whether they should stay on their anti-inflammatories or stop them. It was hard to give them the right answer. My experience was unique but it had raised awareness about how damaging ongoing medication can be to anyone.

Sometimes the calls were from the media too. They would just ask how I was doing and get quotes for their next articles. I was featured in many newspaper reports and I really hoped that awareness of my situation would help others make better decisions. Many of the articles focused on the fact that I had been a sportswoman and taken anti-inflammatories. The story attracted the attention of some top sports coaches and trainers and sparked a debate within the medical and sporting professions regarding the use of such drugs and the damage they could do to the kidneys. The press was lapping it up and one full-page spread had the shocking headline 'Drugs Ruined Me', with a really disappointing photo of me. Shock value, I guess.

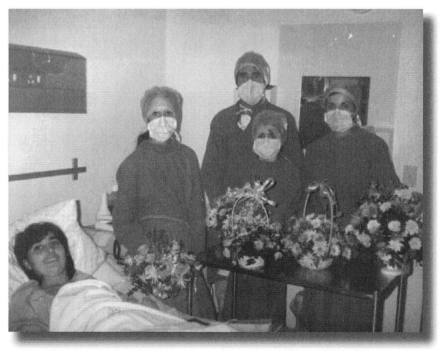

A different sort of family photo. This was taken a couple of days after my first transplant. Can't even see if my family is smiling behind those masks.

Morning tea in the Transplant Unit with Fiona, Sister Pam,
Professor Del Kahn and one of my friendly nurses.

Throughout my time in the Transplant Unit I made sure I got involved in all decisions about my treatment. I had plenty of debates with the morning medical team and often questioned their choices of medication levels, learnt about the drugs and discussed my future with them. Knowing that I would be responsible for the future success of my kidney transplant, I wanted to make sure that I was in the best possible place both physically and mentally to make this kidney last. I was like a sponge and consciously absorbed everything they said, asked questions constantly and learnt more every day.

It wasn't all medical talk and much of the time was spent talking about my past tennis career and potential future careers. They were positive that I would lead a full and healthy life. This gave me hope and added to my determination to fly home as soon as possible. Often the registrar would stay back and talk with me. Fiona, the new transplant coordinator did the same. Both made time during the day to visit and check up on me, which was great and very much appreciated as it broke up the long, boring and sometimes lonely hours. Over the coming years, Fiona became a close friend during the many months I spent in Groote Schuur. It was good to have a confidante when my parents weren't around.

However, soon it was time to go home and start my new life with my new kidney. Leaving the security of my hospital room was both scary and exciting. I was returning home a totally different person. It was my chance to restart my life and make the most of this incredible gift. The pressure to do that right was enormous. I didn't want to waste a moment.

Transplant recipients often talk about being on an incredible high in the days and weeks after a transplant. The knowledge that, after months or even years on a road to nowhere, you have now been shunted back onto a road with a future is so liberating and empowering.

Not every one is lucky enough to get a second chance. I was going to make it count.

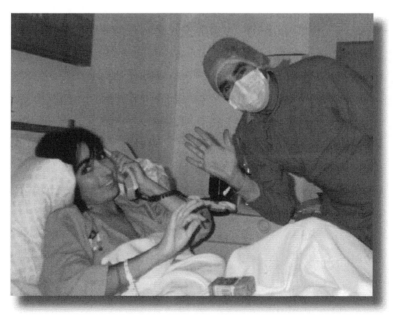

The phone was always ringing and that's Dad behind the mask.

The hundreds of cards kept coming - we ran out of space in my room. They really brightened up my little hospital haven.

11
Finding My Way

'Healing may not be so much about getting better, as about letting go of everything that isn't you – all of the expectations, all of the beliefs – and becoming who you are.'
– Rachel Naomi Remen

I felt reborn! Despite the continuing drug regime and regular hospital visits for blood tests and blood-pressure checks, I was very happy to be free of dialysis and all the trauma that came with it. I arrived home to find my room sparkling, full of roses, flowers and many cards waiting to be opened and read. Mitzi was hovering around my feet while Dad was worrying that she would give me some kind of infection and tried unsuccessfully to shoo her out the room.

I settled into bed after my tiring flight home and spent the afternoon being pampered by my family with tea and cake. Gabby and Mitzi snuggled up beside me and were content; they had their mommy home at last.

The following morning reporters from the *Daily Dispatch*, our local newspaper, arrived. My story was still capturing the hearts of those who knew me and my family in East London. It had all the right ingredients: shock, hope and miracles. The journalists decided to take photos of me riding the indoor bicycle, which was similar to the hospital ones I had used, looking as if I was well on the road to recovery. To most people who saw that photo on the front page I must have appeared nothing like someone who had just had major transplantation surgery. I had the biggest grin on my face and looked a picture of health.

Apart from some discomfort around my abdomen where the kidney had been placed, I felt fantastic. A transplanted kidney is connected to the ureter and main artery, making the area near the groin just to the left or right of the belly button the easiest and safest place to put it. A person's own kidneys are buried deep in the back behind muscle and are very seldom removed unless they are cancerous, covered in cysts, or causing pain or discomfort. My own kidneys had shrivelled to the size of prunes.

The high dose of immunosuppressive drugs I was on meant that I was extremely susceptible to germs and viruses. Regular visitors made me feel special and loved but I was only allowed to see a limited number of people at a time and anyone with a cold was told to stay away. I had to remember not to do the South African thing and greet friends with a kiss on the lips. Instead I would turn my cheek quickly and apologise. 'Sorry, no kisses. Only hugs allowed.'

I had to steer clear of confined and crowded public places, in particular cinemas, shopping centres and enclosed or windowless rooms. Of very real threat were the many cases of undiagnosed tuberculosis in the region. It was important that I didn't contract this illness and that I be very mindful of the places I visited and the people I came into contact with. The last thing I wanted was to lose my kidney after all that we had gone through, so I followed the rules and my parents were particularly protective, always aware of what was happening around me.

One point I was unwilling to compromise on was keeping my pets near me. At that time doctors had mixed opinions about the risk pets posed to transplant patients. For me, the psychological benefits of having my dogs and cat on the bed far outweighed the negatives.

I wanted to live as normally as possible and enjoy my renewed energy, but I had to be very patient during this period of adjustment and quarantine. I started to take morning walks around the block with my Jack Russell while my family went back to their usual routines. Thelma, our caring family nanny, made me tea at every opportunity and ensured I was comfortable.

Slowly my appetite improved and Dad was pleased to see me eat full meals again. Thelma no longer had to peel and soak a potato separately for me and I could at last have the same food that my family enjoyed. I was able to eat without restrictions – a real treat.

Mich, Pete and I had bonding sessions at 4.30 p.m. every day when we would watch the soaps on TV. Dad would arrive home at 5 p.m. to receive barely a greeting from any of us as we sat glued to *Days of our Lives*. Ridiculous as these shows were, it was great to have something to look forward to during my long hours of being at home on my own while I recovered and got my strength back.

*

My first invitation to speak came a few months after the transplant. My former high school, Hudson Park, was having a sports awards ceremony and invited me to speak to the students and hand out the prizes. By now I had developed the tell-tale chubby cheeks and muscle-wasted skinny legs that being on a high dose of steroids produces. A lot of extra hair was making its appearance on my body, including my face. This meant I was lacking in confidence and felt nervous at the prospect of speaking to people when I didn't look my best. But it did not deter me and I bravely arrived at the assembly to share my story.

The speech began with, 'I remember, not long ago, sitting in this hall, just like all of you now, and I was filled with hope and dreams. I had my life laid out before me and I was determined to reach the goals I had set for myself. I didn't even give a thought to the possibility that anything could go wrong with my plan. What I hadn't taken into account was that life is like a journey along a road that is filled with twists and turns, rocky patches and even potholes. My map only had that one road and there was no backup plan if I got lost. As a young woman with huge dreams, I didn't believe anything could go wrong. What I didn't realise was that sometimes things don't go according to plan...'

Being a sportsperson with big dreams, I was able to describe how hard it was when these dreams were shattered by the news of my kidney failure. My message to them was simple: no matter what happens to you in life, you need to believe that you can handle the challenges you will face, find the strength to keep moving forward and overcome anything that gets in your way. If necessary you need to find a new road to success or redefine your dreams and goals. Change is a part of life.

I was amazed what an effect my talk had on the students. You really could have heard a pin drop in the hall. Remembering what it was like to be in assemblies listening to speakers myself, I recalled how much we used to fidget, whisper and long for them to finish. Instead, I felt appreciated and listened to. It gave me a sense of the power I had to influence an audience and share an important message.

I was also invited to speak to the children at Clarendon Primary School, at their awards assembly. They knew much of my story through Mom, their school principal.

The talks gave me purpose. They were a way of expressing the life-changing experience I had been through in a real and down-to-earth way. They gave me a chance to share how important it is to take care of your kidneys, how precious these little-talked-about organs are and what an incredible medical advance transplantation is. So few people really know what kidneys do. Even fewer know a transplant recipient personally. I was able to give people more information to really think about organ donation and make an educated decision about the issue.

The talks also gave me the perspective to realise that what had seemed impossible only months previously had in fact happened and I had survived. I had overcome months on dialysis and received a life-saving kidney transplant. I paid tribute to my donor and their family who had so generously agreed to donate a kidney to allow me to live. The rules of transplantation and organ donation mean you are not allowed to know your donor and it was hard to know how to thank them. All I could do was live my life and make the most of this special second chance. I was able to prove that overcoming obstacles and challenges in life was definitely possible with support and the right frame of mind.

I still had a lot of questions and now more time to consider them. Had I perhaps become ill for a reason? Maybe I had been taking life too easily, floating around in my own little bubble with no concern for others. Being ill had changed all that. It helped me appreciate the wonderful, caring and supportive people around me. I wanted to make the most of this incredible opportunity called life.

*

Soon I was strong enough to start working again and to return to university. Attending lectures and seeing everyone made me feel a bit more normal and I didn't have to skip any classes for dialysis. It was a good time and although I was still fragile and taking each day as a new beginning, I was feeling great.

Eating and drinking anything I wanted was such freedom. It also meant I could go out with friends and enjoy myself with a less restrictive attitude. Late nights weren't as hard and I danced to my heart's content at our local nightclub, revelling in my new-found energy and health. I was using every minute to celebrate my life and I am sure I was better company than I had been in previous months. The drama for now, was on hold.

I started helping Mom at her school with hockey coaching and towards the end of the August was asked to go to Port Elizabeth and coach the team that was playing in a mini tournament there. Port Elizabeth (PE) is about three hours' drive from East London and many of my school friends were studying there, at the University of Port Elizabeth. My schoolfriend Ingrid was living in the dormitory on campus and she was happy for me to stay the night. Grant offered to come with me. He was going to stay with our friends Ryan and Michael, who were in the men's dormitory. It was a happy reunion for us all.

The week before we drove down I noticed some blood in my urine. It wasn't like the blood from menstruation, more like dark red wee. I needed to empty my bladder all the time, even shortly after I had just gone. I hoped it was nothing serious and willed it to go away. My medication had been increased recently because my creatinine was a little high. Nothing too alarming but worth keeping an eye on just three months post transplant. The medical team had also decided to change my immunosuppressant to a cheaper generic version due to the long-term cost of cyclosporin.

I didn't tell Grant about my red wee as it was a bit weird to share something like that and I didn't want to alarm him. Dr G sent me to a local urologist who examined me and said I had cystitis and that it should clear up with a dose of antibiotics. I went to PE hoping the same thing.

It was an uncomfortable weekend. My bladder burned, I needed the loo far too often and I started to feel really awful, but I didn't say anything to my friends. Since the transplant I hadn't gained the weight that we'd expected I would, being on steroids. Instead I was painfully thin, fitting into jeans that I had worn when I was fourteen. However, I still had a puffy face, which I was sure screamed out to the world that I was a transplant recipient. While I tried to act normal and jovial, deep down I was becoming concerned. There was something wrong.

In the toilets of a PE nightclub the reality of my situation made me grimace. Surrounded by giggling, tipsy university students having a good time made me feel like an alien. What would these girls think if they knew I was a kidney transplant weeing blood? Suddenly embarrassed, I wanted to hide in the toilet with my fat face, hairy body and skinny chicken legs. I looked like an experiment. My second-chance joy was wavering. I felt upset, robbed of my youth and incredibly abnormal. This was not what I'd expected – transplantation was meant to be my ticket to a healthy future. When would I start to feel normal again? All I wanted was to teleport home to my safe and cosy bed with Gabby by my side.

Ingrid shared some disturbing news before I left PE. We had worked out who my organ donor was, simply by putting two and two together from the stories that had appeared in the local paper on the same day as my transplant. The sister of my organ donor lived on the same floor as Ingrid at the university. I was terrified that I would bump into her in the corridor. What would I say? As much as I wanted to show her how grateful I was for my kidney, I was not sure how she would react to seeing me. My donor was uppermost in my mind on most days. Without the generous gift of a kidney, I most certainly wouldn't have been living the life I was. In fact I might not have even been there at all.

A few days after I returned from PE I was admitted to St Dominic's Hospital for a bladder biopsy. Dr G wanted to know what was causing this alarming and very serious case of cystitis. While Mom was packing all my things into the cupboard beside my bed, I was undressing into a theatre gown. One of the nurses entered to give me a pre-med to relax.

'*Jislaaik*, you have a lot of hair, hey?'

I shot daggers at her with my look while I hid my hurt and said, 'Gee, thanks for that. If you were on as many drugs as me you would also look like a baboon.'

When she didn't apologise I asked her to leave while I got undressed. She walked away in embarrassed silence and I pleaded with Mom to take me home straight after the operation to avoid more torturous stares from the staff. There was no way I was spending one moment more than necessary in that place. Mom, true to her word, repacked my things, carried me out as soon as I woke from the bladder biopsy and drove me home. Thank heavens I only weighed 45 kg.

The results of the biopsy identified that my severe cystitis was being caused by the high doses of immunosuppressants. Dr G ran more tests to confirm what he was also beginning to suspect – that my precious kidney was starting to reject.

In a last-ditch attempt to save it, I was given intravenous steroids – a huge dose over three days. Within minutes of the drug coursing through my veins the room in the Renal Unit turned a bright white-blue and I could taste the bitter substance on my tongue. The side effects of this medication just got worse.

*

Back at home waiting to see if the steroids would save my kidney, Mom and I decided to tackle the hair issue.

I had always been hairy as a child and had competitions with the boys at school to see who had the longest and thickest arm hairs, but nothing had prepared me for the hair that had appeared on my body as a result of the enormous doses of immunosuppressive drugs. A shadowy moustache had developed on my upper lip and I couldn't deny it, the nurse was right: I had a huge amount of hair all over my body, including in strange places such as my earlobes, my back and my tummy.

The hair on my head became extremely thick and healthy despite the nasty habit I had developed of playing with it and pulling it out when lying in hospital with idle hands. Only the palms of my hands and my feet were hairless – just like a chimpanzee!

I had already taken drastic measures to remove my facial hair, suffering through a full face wax that left my skin red and stinging for hours afterwards. We now bought a hair-removal contraption that had two sides of fine sandpaper which you had to rub on your skin. I had seen it advertised on TV as a painless, simple way to remove hair. I settled myself on a chair in the bathroom while Mom began rubbing it in circles around my back. After a while she started looking concerned. All that was happening was that little knots were being created. The hair seemed to gel together rather than come off. She picked at the knots to pull the hair out, which was not only painful but irritating.

'This isn't working, Helen.'

'Shit, Mom, keep rubbing. Maybe it takes a little while.' I was determined to get rid of the fluff on my body. The knots on my arms were thick and stuck. I couldn't leave them there.

We tried getting the knots off by rubbing my back with soap and water while I stood under the shower, but the problem was only compounded. We were getting desperate and I was feeling raw and tender.

'I think we are going to have to use hair-remover on your body.'

What the heck, I couldn't go around with knots all over my body.

I walked around the house naked, covered in Nair, with Pete complaining again about my stench – 'You smell like a toilet drain'– and my body tingling from the cream. It took a while to rub off the Nair and with it the remainder of my hairy knots. I looked and felt like a freshly plucked chicken and appeared even thinner with my smooth, now hairless body.

On 9 September 1991 I turned twenty-one. It was a milestone for both me and my family, who had not been sure I would even make it to the landmark age most youngsters long for. At last I was legal in all senses of the word, not that it mattered much to me at the time. I had never been a big drinker and since my kidney failure was consuming very little alcohol anyway. I was losing confidence and felt positively ugly. I was becoming weak again and disinterested in food. The steroids caused the familiar unpleasant taste in the mouth which made all food unpalatable. Nevertheless Mom and Dad were determined to give me a party.

About fifty people came to the celebration, many of them friends who had supported us through the challenging last year. It was a wonderful Sunday with a typical South African *braai* held in our large garden and around the swimming pool. It started at lunchtime and finished well into the night. It was a gorgeous sunny spring afternoon and I worked my way around the groups of friends sitting in the garden, enjoying my special day. We didn't make a big deal about the challenge of rejection that I was facing. We wanted to remain positive and keep hopeful that I could overcome this little setback. The photos are still hard to look at – they highlight my fat face and skinny legs. The amazing thing was that not one of the guests commented on my looks or made me feel uncomfortable in anyway. They all celebrated with enthusiasm the fact that I was alive to enjoy this milestone.

Celebrating my 21st with all our special friends.

My sister Michelle and me popping champagne at my 21st. My face is enormous from the huge doses of steroids I was receiving to prevent rejection. It was a fantastic day but my family and I knew that there was a battle on my hands to save the kidney.

12
Accepting Loss

'I have no intention of dying. In fact, it will be the last thing I do!'
- Milton Erickson

Nothing worked to stop the rejection of my new kidney. The next couple of months were to be one of the most testing periods of my life. I learnt what it was like to face the prospect of having no future. Losing my transplanted kidney brought a set of medical challenges that tested my strength of character. It made me realise just how much fight I had in me. I was determined to survive. But there were moments when I thought I would die. In fact there were rumours that I already had.

It was a sad day when I caught the plane back to Cape Town and Groote Schuur on my own, knowing that my kidney was failing. Could I really handle going through all this again? It had only been four months since my transplant – barely enough time to get used to my exciting new life. But now the area around the new kidney was tender and aching. I did my best to avoid looking at it or touching it.

Mom and Dad said they would drive down once they knew more about the prognosis and plan of attack. They promised to call Marion and Ian, our wonderful supportive friends in Cape Town and let them know I was going to be in Groote Schuur again. At least they could bring me treats. I was eating so little now and had lost an enormous amount of weight. I looked anorexic, if you ignored the fat face.

I was given my old room in the Transplant Unit, which was a relief. It felt like home and I loved the nursing staff and doctors on the ward. Professor Swanepoel looked grim and very serious. His shock at my appearance was plain to see

'How are you, Helen?' he asked as he sat down gently beside me on the bed. 'Not so good, I hear?'

I wanted to cry.

'Hi, Prof Swanepoel. I feel pretty crappy. Please tell me you can save my kidney?' I pleaded with him, fighting away the tears.

'Well, we need to find out what is happening first, so I must do a biopsy.'

'Please, not another one! They hurt so much. Can't you check the kidney some other way?'

'No, Helen. Sorry. Anyway, it is nothing like the biopsy on your own kidneys. Remember, this kidney is not yours and has none of your nerves attached. The graft is right near the surface so you will hardly feel a thing.'

My transplanted kidney was situated on the lower right-hand side of my abdomen, just below the skin and to the right of my belly button. You could actually see the slight bump in my tummy, which was more prominent now because I was so thin.

He got up and left me then to stave off further arguments. He knew how much I hated needles. A few minutes later he returned with Sister Pam and a tray of utensils.

'You are going to do it *now*? *Here*?' I asked in amazement.

'Yup. Nothing to it.'

Sister Pam helped set up the tray while he scrubbed down and then they started. I was petrified of the pain that I was sure would follow. My body was tense and I struggled to breathe. Sister Pam let me squeeze her hand while I closed my eyes and tried to mentally transport myself to a tropical island far, far away.

The local stung a little and then he continued. The pain was not so much from the needle but more from the pressure on the already sensitive and aching area around the kidney. I couldn't feel pain in the kidney, he was right. However, the whole process still made me panicky. I shuddered with revulsion. I really hate biopsies but, much to my relief, it was over in a few minutes and I was able to breathe again.

Bed rest for twenty-four hours and more sleep while I waited for the news.

The results were not good. In fact, they were dreadful.

The whole team came to my room the next morning to break the news: Prof Swanepoel, Prof Kahn and Dr Pascoe.

'Helen, your kidney has failed. There is nothing we can do. It has solidified and in fact most of the sample was black. I am afraid it has to come out before you get an infection. We also need to get you back on dialysis.'

I didn't know what to say. I couldn't scream and shout, 'Why me? Why now?' and I couldn't argue with them or make them do anything to change the sad facts. The results were clear and my life with this kidney was over. Dialysis was the only way to keep me alive.

'My fistula packed up a few weeks ago,' I said meekly. It had suddenly stopped working for no reason; it might have got blocked while the kidney was rejecting or my now raised blood pressure might have caused it to collapse.

The three doctors had a discussion amongst themselves.

'Okay, well, what I think we should do is organise a session on the machine as soon as possible and we better insert a subclavian catheter in the opposite side to your last one.'

'Okay. But if you puncture my lung, I will definitely run away.' I half-smiled.

'Don't worry, Helen, I have done many catheters, you will be fine.' Prof Swanepoel was confident as he left the room.

*

Mom and Dad drove down as soon as they heard that the kidney had rejected and I was in need of dialysis again. They were there in time for me to start my first session and waited outside the Dialysis Unit while Prof Swanepoel tried to put in a catheter. He was dressed in the usual green garb and a tray of utensils was laid out by a nurse that I didn't know. Memories of the last subclavian catheter were still fresh in my mind. I just hoped that Prof Swanepoel was going to have better luck than Dr G. I was so tired and barely aware of what he was doing. Concentrating on curbing the nausea, I didn't have the energy to protest. I let them carry on without a murmur.

Prof Swanepoel tried three times to insert a catheter into the area around my left collarbone. Instead of asking him to hurry, I begged him to keep trying.

'Don't give up,' I urged. 'You can do this!'

'This is not going to work, Helen. I am sorry, but I can't try again.'

'Please try, there must be some way.'

'Your vein is twisted – there is no chance. I am really sorry.' He sighed.

Unbelievable! How was that possible? Just when I'd thought it couldn't get any worse, it had.

The dejected doctor walked out of the ward ashen-faced and told Mom and Dad, who had already overheard my pleas. He had never failed before. He said that he would now have to try in the femoral vein in my leg. He had no choice.

This was even more frightening. I was fed up and wished that for once something would go right.

After a few attempts he managed to place the catheter in the femoral vein in my leg. These catheters block easily and have to be removed after five days. Over the coming weeks in Groote Schuur, I had four of them. Two on the right, two on the left. The catheter was placed right in the groin so it was impossible to walk without potentially causing a blockage or damaging it. It made moving very difficult. I was forced to lie still and, if absolutely necessary, hobble around. Being flat on my back for weeks was challenging and boring.

The surgeons then removed my rejected kidney. I was upset to discover they had used real stitches. In the stress of it all, I had forgotten to mention that I wanted dissolving ones. Not long after surgery I developed an infection in the wound and was given a lot of antibiotics to treat the septicaemia. My temperature raged and I was still battling to eat. My body was really struggling to fight the infection because I was so weak from the high doses of immunosuppressants.

A week after the kidney was removed, the vomiting started. All it took was a sip of water and a few minutes later the liquid would rush back up. I had been moved into a general ward because they needed my bed in the Transplant Unit. The care was not as specialised there and despite having a private room, I was generally ignored. The nurses were overworked and disinterested and thought I was spoilt and pampered too much by my family and friends. Because of my femoral catheters, I needed help with everything. Even though I had had my room rearranged so that I could reach most of what I needed from my bed, I still couldn't cope easily. The nurses soon got fed up with hearing my bell and in the end I didn't bother using it. I preferred to suffer than hear their comments and impatience. I was helpless, unable to move and totally at their mercy. At times I had to vomit into a mug next to my bed because the staff wouldn't come when I called for a dish. I was vomiting so often that they just didn't care anymore.

All I could manage to eat was soup and even then only little sips before throwing it up again. One evening after a long day of dialysing and vomiting I asked one of the nurses if I could have some hot water for my Cup-a-soup. She stomped off in a huff, only to return an hour later (after I reminded her) with a small cup of lukewarm tap water. My soup just floated on the top and that was the end of my supper.

Mom and Dad did all they could to ensure I was comfortable. When they were able to be in Cape Town they brought me books, a radio and my pillow; they stuck all my cards on the wall and filled my room with flowers sent by friends. They even bought me a toaster and a television. The poor shop assistant had to come to the hospital to set up the TV because we couldn't get the channels to work – that must have been the weirdest house call he had ever made.

Once the TV was installed my popularity on the ward increased, but mostly with the evening shift and cleaning staff. They often sat around my bed and watched shows in my room while I slept. I know the nurses spoke about me and thought I was getting royal treatment. None of them had dealt with a young kidney patient before and I don't think they really believed I was seriously ill. Neither my family nor I cared what they thought. Anything that might help get me through this horrendous period was worth trying.

In the first few days nurses took the time to help me wash, again simply because it was hard for me to do this lying down. When one of them laughed at my hairy chest I decided that I would try to wash myself and told them not to worry. My body hair, which was now worse than ever, seemed to be a source of much amusement. But it was far from funny. It was very difficult to wash myself and I couldn't sit or stand. Mom would give me a hand when she visited because no one else offered to help again.

My parents couldn't stay with me all the time as they both had to work and care for my younger brother and sister. They took turns to travel to Cape Town, either by plane or by car – it was a long day of driving. It was not easy when they were not there as I relied on them so much for everything and felt incredibly alone at times. Thanks to our amazing friends in Cape Town, however, there was always someone to visit me or bring me what I needed. My aunt Jen even flew out from England to spend six weeks with the family and helped look after things at home.

I was at an all-time low. I became severely malnourished and was fed through a nose tube. This lasted a day – vomiting with a nose tube is not fun. A drip became the only way to get fluids into me at least.

When the pain started in my chest, it became difficult to breathe let alone move. Things were getting really challenging and I wasn't sure how much more I could tolerate.

The perplexed doctors sent me for numerous tests: a cystoscopy to check my gall bladder, a laparoscopy to check my stomach, scans of my pancreas and X-rays of my abdomen. Finally they discovered a large cyst on my pancreas, which could be causing my vomiting and pain. A biopsy confirmed that this was fortunately benign (my first bit of luck), but it needed to be aspirated. I was treated for pancreatitis with more antibiotics and the cyst was removed. However, my pain and vomiting continued. We believed all these additional symptoms were brought about by a combination of factors: my body reacting to the large quantity of immunosuppressants, exhaustion from fighting the rejection and my lack of kidney function. I was extremely weak, malnourished and exhausted. My body was losing strength daily.

Nearly every day brought a new medical challenge. My haemoglobin was dangerously low again so every second day I was injected with EPO – this time I qualified for the liquid gold. I loathed the thrice-weekly injections and decided it was better and less painful to have them in my arm than my thigh. I had to endure these jabs for six months.

Ironically, I began to see my thrice-weekly dialysis as something almost to look forward to. It got me out of my dreary, friendless ward and into the Dialysis Unit for a few hours, a welcome change of scene and a chance to interact with the more caring kidney nurses again.

After a month of searching for answers, the renal team advised Mom and Dad that they should fly back down to Cape Town. I was in a very serious condition. The doctors were running out of options. This could be the end.

I had some idea that things were serious because of how I felt, but even in the darkest hours I couldn't quite believe that my life was over. There was so much I still wanted to do if I ever got the chance. So many places I wanted to travel to, so many experiences still to have. Every morning I woke up relieved to be alive for another day.

I tried to keep telling myself that I could get through this. Like a mantra, I repeated the inspiring words that Sherylle Calder, my former coach on the SA hockey squad, had written me in a note: 'I know you have a reserve of power you never dreamed of'. She had also included a poem by Laine Parsons, which ended with the important lines: 'It's up to us/...to push/ the clouds away'.

*

In a last-ditch effort to stop the vomiting, my gall bladder was removed. The renal team joined the surgeons in the operation and placed a permanent catheter in my abdomen so that I could try peritoneal dialysis. Staying on haemodialysis was going to be impossible unless they found a long-term solution for needle access. I couldn't use femoral catheters indefinitely and lying on my back for the rest of my life was not going to work either.

Peritoneal dialysis differs from haemodialysis in that it is done by using your peritoneal membrane, which is the sac that encases your abdominal organs. A litre (or sometimes two) of dialysis fluid is fed into this cavity via the catheter. By the process of osmosis, the toxins of the body are drawn through the peritoneal membrane and into this fluid. After a few hours the fluid, now full of waste particles, is drained and the cavity is refilled with another litre of fresh dialysis fluid to start the process again.

Three days after the operation, I had my first session of peritoneal dialysis. The nurse scrubbed her hands and starting laying out contraptions, equipment and fluid on a little table near my chair. A large bag filled with dialysis fluid (a saline-type solution that encourages osmosis) was attached to the catheter in my stomach. I watched her clean and re-dress the open wound in my tummy where the catheter went into my peritoneum. It was just a hole. Very weird. I found it very difficult to look at and shuddered when the nurse said that I would have to do the same thing myself in a few weeks' time. Aagh, I didn't like stitches and definitely didn't like holes in my body either!

It felt quite odd when the first bag of fluid flowed through the catheter. My tummy felt full and I could hear gurgling as the liquid flowed around my organs. I had to sit for four hours reading and sleeping until they were ready to drain the fluid and start the process all over again.

I soon came to appreciate how clever peritoneal dialysis (PD) is: it's a far gentler form of treatment than haemodialysis and helped do the job of my failed kidneys quite well. Unlike haemodialysis, which is normally done three times a week for four hours at a time, peritoneal dialysis is a continual process that takes place in the body all day, every day. From then on, I always had a litre of dialysis fluid in my peritoneal cavity and I always had a bag attached to the catheter.

It was important for me to learn absolutely everything about peritoneal dialysis. When I was eventually allowed back home, I would be the only patient on peritoneal dialysis in East London. There was no one who knew how to give this treatment in my home town so my family and I would have to manage my dialysis alone or via phone to Cape Town. Training would take at least a month. Changing the bag of fluid, which I had to do four or sometimes five times a day, was an intricate and time-consuming process:

1. Warm up a fresh peritoneal dialysis bag in the microwave for one minute to get it to body temperature (cold fluid would hurt).

2. Wash hands three times from fingertips to elbows using disinfectant soap.
3. Set up tray of equipment and clean each piece and surface with alcohol.
4. Wash hands again.
5. Open valve on catheter, drain fluid out of tummy into the bag currently attached to the catheter.
6. Detach bag and set aside for the waste fluid to be flushed down the loo.
7. Attach new, warmed bag of fluid to the catheter and hang it on a drip stand to encourage flow.
8. Let the new, clean fluid flow into the peritoneal cavity; close catheter once the bag has emptied (usually after about twenty minutes), fold it and store it in underwear to the side of the hip bone.
9. Wash hands and clean equipment again before putting it all away.

The whole exchange process took about an hour. The PD nurses watched over my every step and if I got one thing wrong I received plenty of verbal abuse and had to start from the beginning again. My sports training had prepared me well for this!

*

During one of my dialysis sessions, the sister-in-charge came to tell me that a minister was there to see me.

'A minister? I don't want to see a minister.'

My great-grandmother had recently died and my memories of her having her last rites read made me panic. I didn't need a minister – yet. I was in no state for a visitor and I really didn't want to see another clergyman from the hospital. As a long-term patient, they tried to visit me every few days and although this was very thoughtful, I was tired of entertaining complete strangers. Not only was it exhausting, I felt very uncomfortable praying in such a public place and the last thing I wanted to hear were my last rites.

'Please tell him that I am not up to having visitors.'

Sister walked away and I tried to sleep. Later that evening Mom mentioned that she had received a call from a friend saying that a minister from our church in East London had been to see me but apparently I had said that I didn't want visitors. He sent his regards and wished me well. I felt terrible that this kind man had made the effort to see me and I had sent him away. My feelings about prayer and religion had not changed. I was really fed up with the promise of a miracle. Many friends believed that if I prayed hard enough, God might grant me healing and my kidneys would recover. I just did not believe it. What I really wanted was to know that my family could cope with this desperate situation. If people really wanted to help me, they could pray that I had the strength to handle everything that was still to come.

My days were a struggle. It took all my energy to smile when visitors kindly spent time with me. As much as I wanted the company, I found it really hard to keep cheery and entertaining. Anyone who has been in hospital themselves might understand what I mean when I say that it is always the patient who has to be the conversationalist – you are automatically the centre of attention. My sense of humour was being tested to the limit, but I did my best to store up stories of the happenings in my hospital ward to share with visitors when they came.

One visitor I never refused was Marion, our faithful Cape Town friend. The first time she came to the hospital she was very distressed at what she found – though I only discovered this much later. 'Your mum had tried to explain to me what you looked like,' she told me, 'but your appearance completed shocked me. Fortunately you seemed to be so "far away" from us that you almost certainly neither noticed nor cared. You had shrunk to just this tiny little body with a head shaped like a rugby ball, covered in long, silky, dark hair, and with dominant thick black eyebrows – I still marvel that I didn't pass out there and then at the sight of you.'

Craig, Ian and Marion's youngest son was just thirteen at the time of my illness. He would visit often with his mom and was really concerned for my wellbeing. So much so that one afternoon while his parents and brother Kim were away he skipped school (including lunch) to come and check up on me. He walked forty-five minutes, about two miles, to Groote Schuur via the freeway. Not even a hooting police van or a concerned family friend stopped him from making his way along this dangerous road to see me.

Once at the hospital, he lied his way past reception and security, then navigated the corridors, unsure whether I would be in my ward or on dialysis. When he finally popped his head around the door to my room, he was hot, sweaty, stressed and exhausted.

'You look terrible!' was all I could manage.

The poor boy found me in a bad state too. I was suffering with a serious case of peritonitis and still struggling to keep anything down.

At the time, I didn't really appreciate the huge effort Craig had made to visit me for just half an hour. He had to get back to school in time for supper or would have been in big trouble. When asked where he had been that afternoon, he just said he was at music practice. What a guy!

The Macs visited me often, though Kim, Craig's older brother, was petrified of hospitals and only came to Groote Schuur once. He was so unnerved by the experience that he wrote a poem about it, 'Groote Schuur – G13', which I've included at the end of the book. The Macs let my family stay at their home in Constantia whenever necessary. They were an absolute godsend. I don't think they realise how much we valued their love and support through such a difficult time. Marion even organised an egg-box mattress to ease my aching, bony body after weeks of lying on an uncomfortable hospital bed. The foam mattress had an egg-box-like surface and made me feel like the princess and the pea – it was heavenly and I slept better than ever after that.

One weekend, the Macs even bravely let me stay at their house, despite all my drains and tubes. The staff at Groote Schuur were going on strike to protest about working conditions and I was going to be left without help in a ward that was virtually closing down for a few days. While I sat happily in the Constantia sunshine enjoying views of the back of Table Mountain, I had no idea of the strain that I was causing their family. They watched me like hawks and my glazed and ashen expression did nothing to ease their worry. Ian and Marion hardly slept that night for fear that I wouldn't wake up in the morning. I, meanwhile, slept well in my comfy bed alongside Mom who was keeping watch all night, delighted to wake to birdsong rather than tea trolleys and blood-pressure monitors. The only thing bothering me was the drain in my side, where my transplanted kidney had been. It was still leaking into a small bag due to the ongoing infection. But being free from the confines of hospital was a precious gift and I was actually grateful for the strike.

*

Slowly I got stronger. Free from the femoral catheter now that I was on peritoneal dialysis, I was able to walk again. I explored the hospital day by day. It was fascinating to watch the lives of the visitors, staff and patients unfold around me. The first time I stepped outside into the car park (I had discovered a little café there that made great toasted cheese sandwiches) and felt the Cape's cool breeze on my skin was heaven. Such a little thing, but real air was just divine. Breathing in the fumes of the car-park air made me smile delightedly. I even found a sunny bench where some of the ambulance drivers would sit and smoke and I relished the feeling of the sun on my pale, grey skin. My nighties and gown did nothing to stop me from escaping the confines of the hospital whenever I could. I didn't care a damn what anyone thought of me hobbling about like someone three times my age, carrying drips or dialysis bags and sitting smiling in the sun.

I visited people in different parts of the hospital, carrying all my paraphernalia with me on my exploratory walks. Having spent so much time in and out of Groote Schuur, I had made a few friends. One of them had lost his leg and I remember sitting by his bedside looking at his foil-covered body and thinking, I am so lucky.

Food still had little appeal so I was given a protein-rich drink called Build-up to increase my calorie intake. My fat face was slimming down but I had developed swollen legs and ankles from protein deficiency. Weighing just 40 kg and now with fat legs was a strange look.

It took me over two months to recover from the ordeal of losing my transplanted kidney and gain enough strength to fly home in early December. It had been a long and challenging journey, but I had pulled through. If I could get through this, I believed I could get through anything. I couldn't have done it without the support of the incredible medical team in Cape Town and the good wishes of all our friends and family.

When I was allowed to go home, Dad came to Cape Town to fetch me. We flew back to East London together. It would have been too tough for me to travel alone. I still wasn't strong enough to climb stairs – anything more than a couple of inches was too much for my muscle-wasted legs. I also needed help with all the stuff I had collected over the last few months, including the TV and mattress. Plus there was a massive amount of dialysis fluid, enough to last me until the rest of my first month's supply arrived by road. A month's supply included four litres of dialysis fluid a day for thirty days, which came to a whopping 120 dialysis bags. Only when the month's supply was delivered did we realise just how much there was going to be. The garage was stacked from floor to ceiling along one whole wall. Cars were moved to the driveway.

It was very exciting yet scary flying home. I had been in Groote Schuur for so long that it had become my safe haven. As much as I hated being in hospital, I had made many friends among the doctors, nurses and cleaning staff. It wasn't going to be the last time I saw them though – there was still a second transplant we were hoping for.

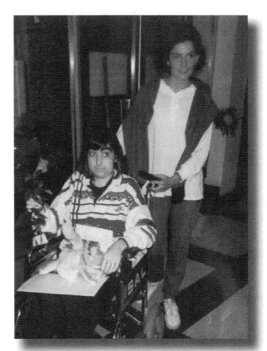

Arriving home from Cape Town after losing my kidney.
My friend Jackie was always there to meet me.

Being welcomed home by the pupils of Clarendon Primary
at the airport.

13
Second Chance – Take Two

'Nobody can go back and start a new beginning, but anyone can start today and make a new ending.'
— Maria Robinson

Although I had been taken off the transplant waiting list because I was too weak and ill to endure transplantation surgery for now, my parents were determined to push for a live-related transplant. The number of organ donors in South Africa in the early 1990s was so tiny that a live-related transplant was going to be my best chance of getting off dialysis. We had decided that Mom would give me one of her kidneys. She felt she would handle it better than Dad. It was a big operation, Dad was still playing a lot of sport and Mom had had enough experience of major surgery in the past to know she could manage.

The doctors were not sure it would be worth the risk. The chances of me rejecting my next kidney, no matter who it was from, were high. They didn't want to put Mom through the pain and trauma of donating an organ that I might reject again. It was not clear whether I was too sensitive to the immunosuppression or whether it was just bad luck that I had lost the first kidney.

My parents, however, were committed and determined. In the months that followed my return from Groote Schuur, Mom and Dad worked hard at helping me get stronger again. We stayed positive. I was not allowed to wallow on peritoneal dialysis. They made sure I did all I could to get strong and healthy in order to handle another transplant. Friends rallied around and parties resumed in our back garden along with regular impromptu *braais*. Our house was always full of happy and vibrant people and it left me little time to feel sorry for myself. The wave of support continued.

Nonetheless, it took me a long time to get over all the complications which came with the rejection. As a family we adapted to my new world of dialysing four times a day. I never went far from home and always made sure I could pop back and do a quick drain and bag change. Our friends got used to seeing me walk around the house with a tube connected to my 'shopping bag', as Dad nicknamed it. If we did go away, like on Christmas Day to the beach, we packed everything but the kitchen sink. We took a special foldable table so I could guarantee that there would be a clean work surface and we heated my bags in warm water when there was no microwave. Filling my stomach with cold dialysis fluid would hurt and if too hot it would burn: it had to be body temperature to minimise the discomfort. On particularly bad days, maybe if it was hot and I had drunk more than my allowance of around 750 ml, I would squeeze in a fifth bag to drain the excess fluid. Often the amount drained into the bag was close to double that which went in to my tummy. I found when I was inland on holiday, the bags drained slowly due to the higher altitude so it would take longer.

Not a week would go by without a medical challenge of some sort. I endured a couple of unpleasant visits to Intensive Care on account of my uncontrollable blood pressure. Kidney disease and high blood pressure are closely linked – one causes the other and vice versa. Mine went so high that I had a few fits, both in hospital and at home. One afternoon, Pete and Mich found me passed out in the passage and I had to be rushed to hospital. How they coped with such situations I don't know. It was after episodes like these that they realised the true extent of my ill-health. Even though they were still so young at just eleven and fourteen, they were becoming very knowledgeable about all things kidney related.

Along with a few bouts of peritonitis (where the peritoneal cavity becomes infected which is common in peritoneal dialysis) I developed another case of pancreatitis when my cyst flared up and had to be re-drained. Days of eating no fat was the only cure for the pain and I remember wondering how there could possibly be so much fat in something as simple as soup. Even an apple has traces of fats, leaving me very little to eat.

128

My ICU stays at the Frere were horrendous and extremely stressful and exhausting for my family. My eyesight had deteriorated again due to my soaring blood pressure and I was reduced to lying flat on my back with a feeding tube in my nose, confined to a room full of beeping machines and patients in comas. It was a very scary place and I was desperate to get home even though I was extremely sick.

Because there was no one trained to perform my peritoneal dialysis and I was in no state to do anything while hooked up to heart monitors, drips and machinery, I had to rely on Mom and Dad to visit me every four hours during the day and night to perform my bag changes. Mom had been trained to do my peritoneal dialysis while we were in Cape Town. She and Dad would arrive in shifts with warmed-up dialysis bags and do what was necessary to keep me alive.

When the staff in the ICU tried to learn my dialysis process it was even more stressful. Even though I kept instructing them to wash their hands three times before starting the procedure, they would ignore me. Fighting them from my blinded position in my bed with tubes in my nose was not easy. But in the end I got my way and I banned them from touching my dialysis catheter (and sometimes even me!) for fear of infection. If I couldn't do it without washing my hands, neither should they!

My catheter blocked at one point during my year of getting stronger and I couldn't drain the fluid from my tummy. This meant that I couldn't dialyse. If I couldn't dialyse I would die. Simple.

Because no one in East London worked with peritoneal dialysis patients, apart from Dr G, I had to fly to Cape Town to have the catheter unblocked. Flying flat on a stretcher at the back of the plane, high above the seats, was a pretty bizarre experience. It was also embarrassing and I avoided people's stares in case I recognised anyone. A nurse accompanied me to keep watch and monitor me throughout the flight. It was a relief to get to Groote Schuur, even if it was in a blaring ambulance at top speed.

While plans were being made for emergency surgery to unblock or replace the catheter, I decided to open the valve and test the draining one more time. If ever I needed a miracle in my life, it was then. And the miracle happened – fluid flowed through the tube!

My catheter had unblocked itself and all was well. We think it must have been the high altitude and pressure in the aircraft. Avoiding more surgery was fabulous news. I was sent home soon after that and instructed to keep building up my strength in readiness for the next transplant.

*

From left, Dieter, Kim, me and Grant, ready to go to the Rhodes University Sports dinner - can't believe I was brave enough to go out with that face!

My days at Rhodes University were over. There was no way I would catch up on all that I had missed during the months I'd been in hospital. Peter Kirsten invited me to a final sporting awards event to celebrate the first year of sport at Rhodes University in East London and Grant escorted me to the special event to keep me secure and confident. It was hard to go out when I felt so weak. I was honoured to receive a special recognition award for my services to sport at the university and felt pleased to be a part of something that would grow in the future. It had been a good experience while it lasted. But no more studying for me. Living was enough of a challenge!

Having never previously had the time or the inclination to try anything that didn't involve sport, now that I couldn't be active, I needed to find something else. Anything that might distract me from the endless hospital visits, dialysis treatment and lonely hours spent at home while everyone else was living their lives was worth trying. I soon began developing my creative side.

It all started with Jenny, one of my parents' lovely friends. I had grown up with her and Nolan's children and we had spent many wonderful holidays together on the Wild Coast of Africa. The men fished while the women enjoyed lazy days on the deserted beaches. We kids made sandcastles, played in the waves and challenged each other to card games around the campfire.

When I was dialysing at home one day, Jenny arrived for a visit with her basket of cross-stitching. She started unloading the intricate work and showed me all the designs, cottons and materials that she used to create her amazing pieces of art. I was soon curiously leafing through the pattern books and holding up examples of her beautiful work. I was surprised at how detailed and fascinating they were and how if you held them at a distance the designs actually looked like paintings. They were incredibly inspiring. Not at all like I expected cross-stitching to be.

Without hesitation she handed me a fattish needle, some coloured thread and a piece of cream material that was made up of woven squares. The picture she gave me was of two little children sitting back to back with a heart above them. The pattern was on a grid and showed the same image but with symbols which corresponded to colours in the key below.

'All you do is take your threaded needle and start in the middle.' I watched Jenny fold the material in four and pick a point on the cream Aida cross-stitch material. She stitched one way and then back the next to make a cross and then did a few more, until I started to see the pattern. I mimicked what she did. It was like painting with threads.

The satisfaction of completing that first piece of cross-stitch was fantastic. I couldn't wait to try something else. We went shopping to Floradale, a large garden centre just out of town, and browsed the vast selection of cottons, materials, patterns and equipment. My imagination ran wild and my creative side was fuelled.

Cross-stitching became my refuge. I spent hours on large comfortable chairs in our sunny garden, stitching gifts for friends and family. It helped make bearable the long periods of solitude both at home and in hospital.

During one of my hospital stays at Groote Schuur I worked on a Christmas sampler for my family. It was a large, complex design with loads of colour and an A to Z of Christmas images. It took me a few months to complete. At the admittance desk on this occasion, I had said I was Jewish rather than Methodist. A Jewish friend had suggested that this would ensure I was delivered home-cooked kosher meals. She knew how little I ate in hospital and it was her way of helping.

The meals were fabulous – she was absolutely right! Memories of my Jewish pre-primary school flooded back and I had no qualms about having faked my religion. There wasn't always someone around to buy me food from the local supermarket and having spent the best part of a year of my life in hospital, anything that helped me cope, and eat, was worth trying.

What I hadn't banked on with this little deception, however, were the visits from the Jewish ladies who actually made the food. They liked to pop in and meet the Jewish patients, to make sure they were happy with the meals and, I suspect, to secretly check that they were indeed Jewish. I had a couple of things against me – my name and the piece of cross-stitch on my bed when they arrived.

Luckily, I thought quickly. I said the sampler was for friends to thank them for all they had done for me and that my Jewish roots were on my mother's side of the family, hence the non-Jewish surname. I could at least be truthful about my time at a Jewish pre-primary school and no one could argue with my large nose! It was a close call though and I made sure they knew how much I appreciated the delicious meals. I hoped that made me a little less guilty too.

Teaching me to cross-stitch was such a wonderful gift from Jenny. Cross-stitching has given me huge pleasure and comfort over the years and is a lot less messy than the pottery I also tried while on dialysis. Getting that mud out of my fingernails was so hard during my four-times-a-day hand-scrubbing that I had to drop that hobby fast. I was also running out of ideas on what to do with my creations. There were only so many peanut bowls that one needed.

*

Finally, sixteen months after I'd been admitted to the Groote Schuur for my first transplant, I was back there again, about to receive from Mom the greatest gift.

Receiving a kidney from anyone is hard, but receiving it from someone who is not only very much alive but is in fact your mother is harder still. I knew the risks and so did she. I had to focus on the positives and keep reminding myself of how amazing it would be to get off dialysis and really live again.

We had to say our goodbyes in the corridor of the Transplant Unit. Mom was on the trolley and the porters were waiting patiently as I tried to find the right words to say good luck. We were both quite dopey with our pre-medications. What on earth do you say to someone who is about to go under the knife to have a perfectly good kidney removed so that you can live? After giving her a hug, I watched her being wheeled away. I felt dreadful.

I wanted this to be over and fast. Going back to my bed, I lay down for the wait and soon dozed off. I woke to find the porters preparing to take me downstairs. They lifted me onto the cold gurney and I watched the ceiling whizz by as they wheeled me along the familiar winding corridors to the surgical ward.

I was parked outside the operating theatre where Mom was still on the table.

'Your mom is doing very well,' the theatre nurse told me. 'The kidney is out and they are preparing to close her up now. Won't be long before you're taken in.'

Tears started and I tried not to look as the door swung open and another nurse appeared. I couldn't bear to see Mom on the surgical table so I squeezed my eyes shut.

The last thing I remembered were bright lights and the voices of the team. I woke up back in the Transplant Unit with a mask over my mouth, tubes everywhere and the familiar beeps of the monitors. It was over. 'Bernie the Bean' had a new home. And Mom and I were both alive!

We had chosen to name my kidney Bernie after my mom, Bernadine. I was used to being called 'the kidney kid', but now we could focus on my kidney instead. Most transplant recipients' name their kidneys and even other organs. It underlines the fact that it's a gift from someone who has provided you with the very precious chance to live again. Bernie was placed on the left side of my abdomen this time, close to my groin and just under the skin. The dissolving stitches I had requested were neatly in place. All was good in the world.

The first few days after surgery are always the hardest. Everything in my tummy hurt. The slightest movement was torture, but I knew Mom's pain would be far worse. I tried my best not to complain. As soon as I was able, I hobbled to Mom's room down the corridor. She wasn't able to move yet: her operation had been far bigger than mine. Removal of a kidney is no easy process as it is buried deep inside the back muscles behind the lower ribs. It is also important that the ureter and blood vessels that are connected to the kidney are kept intact so that they can be reattached to the recipient's body. Nowadays transplant surgery is often performed by keyhole surgery, which is minimally invasive and leaves the donor with only a few little scars rather than one large cut. Mom, however, had a 20-cm scar that stretched from the front of her abdomen to her back.

Mom was in pain, I could tell. She was putting on a brave face but while I was up and about, walking and washing myself, Mom had yet to leave the bed on day two. The transplant had transformed me – my blood results were excellent, I was producing lots of wee (usual excitement about this!) and I was clear-headed and energised. Mom was sick from the anaesthetic, sore and missing a kidney.

We were still attracting a lot of media attention. Reporters from the national television station SABC arrived in the second week to interview and film Mom and me in our hospital beds. They wanted to cover the story, partly because it was still rare for a family member to donate a kidney in South Africa and also because I had created quite a media storm as a sportswoman who had suffered kidney failure as a result of anti-inflammatory abuse. Neither of us were media trained and I remember thinking that we must be mad sitting on a bed in our pyjamas being interviewed for the national news. The last thing I had expected in my life was to become famous on account of an illness; it would have been so much better if it had been because of something great I'd achieved. In the event, one of the few comments which was used was 'I don't want any more Christmas presents – this kidney covers me for life!' That sentiment lasted only until Christmas of course!

After a week, Mom was allowed to go and stay with the Macs. I spent a couple more weeks in hospital so that my immunosuppression levels could be monitored. Getting the dose and mix of immunosuppressive medication right is key. Many immunosuppressants are nephrotoxic, which means they can cause damage to the kidney in the long run. Having learnt our lessons from the first transplant, I was given just a short dose of steroid treatment and put on the more expensive cyclosporin along with traditional azathioprine. No more talk about ketoconazole. The steroids would be reduced and I would be weaned off them after a few months. We worked to keep all my drug doses very low, which would also help to keep the side effects to a minimum.

Back at her East London home, Helen Philpott works out on an exercise bike yesterday as part of her recovery programme.

EL transplant patient home

Daily Dispatch Reporter

EAST LONDON — A young East London woman returned home yesterday after two weeks in recovery at Cape Town's Groote Schuur Hospital where she underwent a mother-to-daughter organ transplant operation.

"I'm recovering well and I haven't had any major setbacks. The next three months are a critical period so I'm going to be taking it one day at a time," Miss Helen Philpott said from her family's Nahoon home yesterday.

Helen, who first underwent a kidney transplant operation in May last year, said she was on a course of drugs to fight her body's possible rejection of the new organ.

She would also be required to give blood samples several times a week while doctors continue to monitor her progress.

Helen said the new organ meant, among other things, a more varied diet.

"Now I can drink as much fluids as I like and bascially eat anything. Before I had to worry about my potassium levels," she said

The plucky 22-year-old, whose promising sports career abruptly ended when she suffered total kidney failure, said she had adapted well to her more relaxed lifestyle but was still able to enjoy cycling and social tennis.

Credit: Daily Dispatch

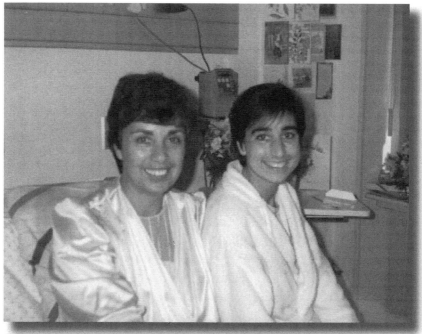

Mom and I a few days after the transplant
which saved my life.

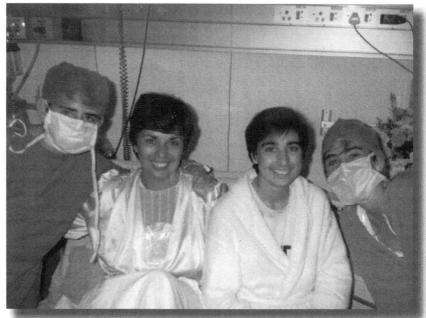

A few days after my second transplant with Mom recovering well.
Pete on the left and Mich on the right behind their masks.

Being free of the PD catheter in my tummy was fabulous. Once my scar had healed, I had the biggest bubble bath and lay in blissful fragrant bubble heaven for ages. My first swim in the pool was also memorable. There was nothing better than floating on a lilo under the hot African sun with my toes dangling in the cool water of our pool. Drinking a whole cup of tea was a treat and I could once again enjoy creamy avocados with tuna salad and chocolate to my heart's content. It took time to indulge, though. As a kidney patient, you are so programmed to avoid these dangerous foods that when you are finally free to eat what you want with a new kidney it is quite scary. Even to this day, I don't eat a lot of chocolate, hardly eat potatoes and don't touch bananas. The only high-potassium food I don't limit is avocados. The fear of potassium overload has never left me.

As I got used to living with Mom's kidney, Bernie, I started thinking about what I could do with my life. It felt great to think of the future once more. The kidney was happy and working well. Nothing about transplantation was guaranteed though. I needed to make the most of my life now and especially while I was well. Living with a new kidney comes with the ever-present risk of the kidney failing or rejecting. Mom was a near perfect match for me, so the chances of rejection were greatly reduced. But the kidney was still a foreign organ living in my body and for the rest of my life there would be the possibility that I could reject it. I knew this kidney was my chance to live again. There was no way I was going to waste a minute. No matter how long I had with it, I would make the most of my life.

The greatest gift Mom was able to give me was hope and the ability to dream again. She freed me from a life of dialysis. The best way I could show her how much I appreciated this incredible generosity was to live my life to the best of my ability.

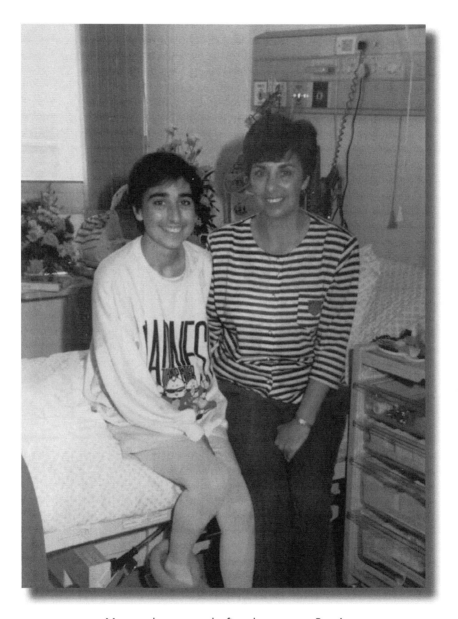

Mom and me, a week after she gave me Bernie.

14
Going for Gold

'Achieving goals by themselves will never makes us happy in the long term; it's who we become, as we overcome the obstacles necessary to achieve our goals, that can give us the deepest and most long-lasting sense of fulfilment.'

– Anthony Robbins

Aunty Zoë changed my life. She wasn't really my aunt but rather a very special family friend whom we knew through years of playing tennis together with her and her family. Her husband George ran a local pineapple farm and we spent many wonderful holidays together on their property on the Busman's River. It literally was on the river – built on stilts over the water – and I loved watching the tide ebb and flow under the house. Playing with my best friend Penny on the river provided me with some of my favourite childhood memories.

Zoë had been desperate to introduce me to the game of golf well before I was due to have the second transplant. She had moved from tennis to golf herself and was convinced it would suit my determined spirit and keep me involved in sport without having to stress my body. I was not so sure. Wasn't golf for retired people? In those days very few youngsters played at the private club in East London.

Once my wound had healed and I was able to walk with confidence and strength, she dragged me out onto a driving range in Beacon Bay, a suburb of East London. Her enthusiasm and determination were so infectious that even before I swung a club I was led to believe I would be good at it. Part of me thought I would just humour her. She was being kind. I didn't really think that golf was going to be my thing.

When I tried to hit the ball it felt foreign and weird. It was so damn small and Zoë's grey and pink club felt awkward in my hand. My swing resembled a hockey shot (not surprisingly) and I was reminded of my earlier goal-scoring days at school. But a hockey ball was so much easier to hit! And you could run with it.

My first instinct was to take a run up before hacking into the ground. But Aunty Zoë was having none of it. 'Keep your feet firmly on the ground. Head down, eyes fixed on the ball and knees slightly bent. Swing those hips and use your whole body.'

I just nodded and thought, how on earth do I hit this weeny, scuffed ball? My head was spinning with everything I had to remember. I felt useless but determined. No way was I giving up.

Zoë was full of praise and encouragement after each dud ball, whether it skidded along the ground or just stayed perched on the precarious tee following one of my air shots. When I finally connected with one of the balls, the joy at having hit it into the air was immense. Who would have thought you could feel such a thrill from hitting a tiny white ball towards a distant random flag?

After a few more sessions at the driving range I joined the Bunnies, a group of beginner ladies who met at the East London Golf Club on Thursday mornings. Most of them were mothers and housewives who had time to spare while their children were at school. Some were just keen to try this latest craze. We all stood on the practice tee determined to show Alan, the local pro, that we had what it took to make a fine golfer.

'Philly, I can see you have that hockey swing in you, but it's not bad, 'Alan commented as he walked past me.

Was that a compliment? My hands ached from the effort and I tried my best to copy what I had seen pros do on TV. Suddenly the game was taking on a unique fascination and I was devouring it from every angle.

After about three weeks of just hitting balls, I really wanted to feel the thrill of a game. A group of us Bunnies convinced Zoë that it was time to try the course at the East London Club.

'Now, my child, just do your best. I don't expect you to get the ball down in par. The first time I played this hole I did it in fifteen.'

Zoë was really trying to keep me positive and patient. This did not stop me from wanting to be great and prove myself to everyone.

My first shot soared through the air and landed gloriously in the centre of the fairway about 100 metres away. Not far, but straight. It was a start and it felt really good! However, it was downhill from there. I managed to sink the ball in ten and learnt the first rule in golf: do not get too cocky.

Soon I became confident enough to go to the driving range in Beacon Bayon my own. I borrowed some clubs from Zoë and began spending a lot of time in the practice area. I met Ross, who was always practising when he wasn't picking up the balls on the hitting area. He had a nice smile and a great swing. And he was company on the long days at the range. It was a lonely game. Having played sport with other competitors for so many years, I found this hard to get used to.

Ross really helped to keep me focused and encouraged me to believe that I could get better with practice. He taught me so much about golf and patiently praised my development. He was funny, kind and a great golfer, hoping to turn professional in time.

One Sunday I joined Ross and his friend Kamal for a game at West Bank Golf Course. Both men were full of generous compliments. Considering they were low handicappers, I kept up with them quite well. After my first nine holes ever, I was hooked.

Once I had my first handicap, a 27, I played on Saturdays with the ladies at East London Golf Club. We had such fun competing against the men every week. I had a regular four ball team and we did lots of talking and laughing. There was plenty of banter, plenty of cross-team betting and even prizes when we managed to play well.

After a couple of months of playing golf, I contacted the South African Transplant Games Association and asked if I could join the team for the next Transplant Games. I'd heard about the Transplant Games while in hospital and was keen to get involved. Prof Kahn had always said I would play competitive sport again. What was stopping me now?

My goal was to play at the World Transplant Games in Vancouver in July, about five months away. My handicap was considered good enough and there was every chance it would be lower by the time I flew overseas. I would be the only female golfer in the team. I was only a few months post transplant, however, and the rules were that you had to be a year post transplant to compete. I just made it with some negotiations at nine months. It also helped that I arranged for my consultant and now friend Dr G to be team doctor. I would have my very own support flying with me.

Having the focus of the Games was so important to my recovery. It kept me motivated and active and, even more vitally, it got me believing in new dreams and possibilities. I was still unsure what my future would hold. I didn't have a career to concentrate on and was finding it extremely difficult to work out what to do with myself. The Games gave me direction and something to look forward to. It felt positive and empowering.

On a Saturday just a couple of months before I was due to fly to Vancouver I played in a club tournament with Aunty Zoë. Afterwards I sat sipping a refreshing glass of chilled passion-fruit juice. My body felt tired but I was exhilarated. Aunty Zoë and I had dovetailed well and ended with a brilliant score. It was sure to be in the prizes.

'Congratulations, you two, showing these men up!' Alan shouted as he walked in to the bar. 'I think plus 9 is the winning score today.'

We looked at each other and Alan in disbelief.

'Surely not?' I exclaimed.

Aunty Zoë seemed less surprised. 'I thought we had a chance, but I decided to keep quiet – didn't want you to get too cocky out there!' She knew what I was like.

Then to my surprise Mom and Dad arrived for a drink too. I hadn't expected them to join us. There was quite a bit of jeering from the men as we went up to collect our prize. It wasn't often that the women won on competition Saturday.

The captain of the club started to speak. 'Many of you will already know that we have a very special lady with us today. She only started golf four months ago and already is taking home the prizes.'

A few snickers floated around the room. I started feeling embarrassed and sensed that eyes were turning towards me. What was going on?

'Helen Philpott received a kidney from her mother, Bernadine, who is also here today. Since then, Helen has not looked back. Zoë got her hooked on golf just a few months after her transplant. As some of you know, Helen plans to represent South Africa at the World Transplant Games in Vancouver, Canada in two months. We thought it only fitting to give her a little assistance and perhaps she will bring a medal home for us.'

Alan then stepped out from behind the captain. In his hand was a set of golf clubs. When I got closer I realised they were the same as, in fact an even better version of, Aunty Zoë's clubs that I had first learnt to play with and had been borrowing on every possible occasion since.

'Helen, the men decided you deserved your own set of clubs. They have all contributed. Play well and we wish you every success in Vancouver. We are very proud of you.'

I didn't know what to say. This was astonishing and such a generous gesture. With tears streaming down my face, I hugged the clubs excitedly and stood at the microphone to thank all the men for their incredible generosity. I was so touched that they had gone to all this trouble for a little squawk like me.

Without thinking, I promised to bring back a gold medal.

My beautiful new clubs were Gary Player, Lady Anvils. The shafts were graphite covered with a beautiful wood effect and the heads were brass blades. There were lilac highlights in the shaft and on the grips. They looked gorgeous, unique and stylish and I couldn't wait to try them out.

*

There were twenty-four of us in the South African team heading to the World Transplant Games in Vancouver and most were kidney recipients. I was the most recent recipient and still had lots to learn about life with a new kidney. My team-mates looked well and fit and surprisingly unlike the typical transplant recipient – I felt very different. My face was still as round as a balloon and had the obvious 'transplant look'.

Hilary, a swimmer in her fifties, had had her kidney for over twenty years, which was hugely inspirational. She had endured skin cancer and her fair skin had suffered under the harsh African sun. Her lip had been replaced by a skin graft and was scarred and puffy. Some of the others had the same sun-spotted skin on their arms and legs. Maybe I would be lucky with my tough, darker skin? I could only hope. The guys were quite hairy, but not unusually so, and the women seemed less so. A good omen for me? Some had lost their muscle bulk because of the catabolic steroids. But generally we all looked normal. Passers-by would be none the wiser. We were walking miracles, testament to the amazing advances of modern medicine, lucky to have been born into a century that had seen the discovery and refinement of the extraordinary science of transplantation.

6 — DAILY DISPATCH, WEDNESDAY, JUNE 30, 1993

EL sportswoman to compete in Vancouver

Credit: Daily Dispatch

It was such a relief having Dr G with us at the Games. He was sponsored by the pharmaceutical company Sandoz and was designated team doctor. He was clearly relishing the respite from his gruelling job at Frere Hospital and it was great to watch him and his wife enjoying their time with us at the Games.

We were staying on the idyllically located University of British Columbia campus. It was almost an island and the views were spectacular. I was sharing a four-bedroom suite on the thirteenth-storey with three other women from the South African team. We were mesmerised by the panorama over English Bay, which on the afternoon we arrived was shimmering in the late sun, framed by forested mountains in the distance. It was drawing near to dusk and the sky was streaked with molten gold and rose – a result, apparently, of volcanic deposits in the air from an eruption years before.

When I crawled out of bed next morning, I was shocked to learn that Hilary had been up since 5.30 a.m. and Danilda, a woman in her thirties who was also a kidney transplant, had already been for a run.

 Pat, our other room-mate, was the team's only liver transplant. She was around forty, and I felt an affinity with her right from the start.

A few of us golfers made our way to the on-campus driving range to hit some balls. We were most impressed with the modern indoor/outdoor structure. There was even a machine to pick up the balls – no African kids running haphazardly in front of the danger zone like back home

Later that day we were taken on a brief tour of Vancouver. The city seemed such a haven of cleanliness, with pine tree-lined streets, electric buses, perfectly kept grass lawns and signs threatening $1,000 fines for littering the pavements (something we could learn from in Africa). There were no plastic packets snagged on barbed-wire fences; no evidence of the brown, barren countryside of the southern winter; no beggars slouching dismally down forgotten alleys. It appeared to be a rich and prosperous place, with something for every taste: ski resorts, parks, sparkling bays and exquisite beaches – even a nudist one, which we stumbled across near our halls of residence.

Preparing for golf at the World Transplant Games in Vancouver 1993.

My fourball at the World Transplant Games.

After a fantastic but emotional opening ceremony, the real work began. I felt supple and strong. This eased my mind a little and made me more confident about the competition ahead. My only dilemma was that everything was tallied in yards, which meant I had to constantly convert the distances in my head.

On competition day I headed to the course and nervously warmed up for my big game. I had promised to deliver gold and now I was regretting my outspoken confidence. I had absolutely no idea how good the other golfers were and this was my first international competition. Who knew what would happen?

I soon found out on the first tee.

'Next on the tee, Helen Philpott from South Africa,' the announcer bellowed.

I took a step up and placed the ball as carefully as I could on my precarious tee peg. I was starting to feel really nervous now and could sense the butterflies having a whale of a time flying around my tummy. This was it.

Deep breath, practise swing, visualise my landing spot, imagine my smooth swing. Go for it! I took an almighty swing at the ball and connected with a thwack. But when I lifted my head I was horrified to see that my ball had only travelled about twenty yards forward. Shit. Not the greatest start and not really a crowd pleaser. Hide me now.

To my relief the rest of the women in my group were not much better, though they definitely hit the ball further than me.

Head down, second shot. Thwack! Same thing happened. Ball travelled about fifty yards and limped to a sad finish, miles from the green. Now I was pissed off. This was not how I was used to playing golf. Driving was my strength. 'Come on, Helen, pull your bloody socks up,' I chastised myself under my breath.

Finally I swung like the golfer I was and hit the ball, landing it on the green then following it with one putt. I was back in the game. Relief. It would have been one hell of a long game of golf if it had continued along those lines.

I absolutely loved the rest of my round with my inspirational four ball. My game came together and I was hitting like a dream, putting balls in from everywhere. I started to feel relaxed and confident. The score I posted was the best I could do on the day and was well under my handicap, which was still 22. I had left nothing on the course. Whatever happened, I knew I had done my best.

To my absolute shock and delight, I discovered I had won – my dream had become reality! I was over the moon. Receiving that gold medal around my neck was one of the highlights of my young life. Just a year previously, I had not been sure if I would live or die and now I was a gold medallist and World Champion Golfer (in the transplant world anyway).

Calling home and sharing this success with my family was so exciting. The media frenzy began before the day was over, despite the time difference. Everyone wanted to hear about my achievement and bask in my joy. I did radio interviews and was called by papers to tell my story. It was a great day and I was proud to have won a medal for my country.

The rest of our week in Vancouver passed very quickly. It was filled with laughter, building friendships with transplant recipients from all around the world and supporting my team to victories in a variety of sports. Now that the apartheid era had come to an end,

South Africa was back on the international sporting stage and made to feel so welcome. It was humbling.

I was also given a very precious gift: hope. Training hard and making sure I was fit and able to go to the World Transplant Games was the biggest goal I had faced since I received a kidney from Mom. I had had to dig deep, draw on my previous sports training and travel with as much self-belief and confidence as I could muster. Being a totally different person to two years previously meant I was also taking a very different attitude. I was now full of wonder and joy, keenly aware of how precious life really is.

Meeting a thousand transplant recipients from all over and hearing their stories and all the incredible challenges that they had to overcome was so inspiring. I have never experienced such determination, positivity and zest for life. The atmosphere was thick with emotion and energy and you couldn't help being affected by it. I now had hope that my life could mean something and I could be something. I just had to think about what that might be.

Golf medalists at the World Transplant Games

Winning Gold at The World Transplant Games in Vancouver, 1993.

The South African team at the World Transplant Games in Vancouver.
Note we stil had the old South African flag.

With old or new kidneys, Helen is a star athlete!

Transplant girl wins gold medal

By BRIDGET MONK

EAST LONDON — She lived for sport, she nearly died for it, and now Border's Helen Philpott is back on the field and striking gold.

The gutsy 22-year-old returned from Canada this week with a gold medal from the World Transplant Games — just 10 months after undergoing a second kidney transplant.

The operation, in which she received one of her mother's kidneys, was the culmination of three years of agony and illness believed to have been caused by a sensitivity to drugs taken for sports injuries.

An elated HELEN PHILPOTT returned to East London this week with a gold medal from the World Transplant Games just 10 months after undergoing a kidney transplant.

Despite two spells of blindness and an inability to walk after her first kidney transplant, Helen said she had set her sights on the Vancouver Transplant Games before receiving her mother's kidney in September last year.

And as she set off for Canada she promised her family and friends she would bring back a medal.

She did — for golf, a sport she only started to learn six months ago, when tennis proved a little too strenuous.

Helen represented Border at diving, gymnastics, hockey and tennis while still at school.

She saw her dreams of a lifetime in sport as a professional or even as a coach shattered just as she seemed about to realise them.

Severe shin splints while she was on a tennis scholarship in Louisiana in the US led to her taking anti-inflammatory drugs which she said were "handed out for any ache or pain" to most of the sports stars there.

Even before her year's scholarship was up, she said, her health deteriorated, aided by three hours of training every day in the intense heat and humidity of the Louisiana summer.

However, it was only three months after her return to South Africa that doctors realised she was undergoing chronic renal failure.

Four or five months of dialysis followed and then came the first kidney transplant.

Her mother, Clarendon Primary School principal Bernadine Philpott, offered to donate one of her kidneys but her daughter refused, not wanting to put her mother through the operation.

However, the first transplant failed and after a year she received the organ she has nicknamed "Bernie" after her mother.

Helen said earning the gold medal at Vancouver was wonderful, but the biggest prize of the trip was her encounter with the "pure guts and determination" of the contestants.

"It must be the only world games where the contestants and spectators clap more for the one who comes in the line last than for the race winner," she said.

Helen, who believes that everything happens for a reason, said her illness had changed her attitude to life.

Sport, while still important, was no longer her number one life.

Instead she had "seen the goodness in people", and was determined to do something meaningful with her life.

"I feel my life has probably been shortened, but that just fills me with a desire to make the best of every moment of it."

Credit: Daily Dispatch

15
Losing a Part of Me

'Never give up, for this is just the place and time that the tide will turn.'
– Harriet Beecher Stowe

Making the most of my trip overseas, I had decided not to go straight home after the Transplant Games. I was going to visit my aunt and uncle in San Francisco and my best tennis buddy from Louisiana, Kristen, who was now back in Florida. The last time I'd seen Kristen was before I got sick. It was probably going to be really strange for both of us because I was now such a different person, even though it had only been two years.

Dr G wanted me to have blood tests before I left Vancouver because I wasn't going straight home. It's good practice in the first year of a transplant to keep having regular blood tests and to stay on top of drug levels and kidney function in order to nip any rejection episodes in the bud.

The tests were so disappointing. My creatinine and urea were way higher than expected and he was worried. I tried not to worry. What good would that do? There was a suggestion that perhaps I should cancel this extra fortnight's holiday, but I was determined to see my family and friends. If things were going to go wrong again, I didn't want to miss the opportunity.

I promised him I would have another blood test in San Francisco and we upped my medication a little to try and combat any potential rejection. This was his greatest concern. If it was a rejection episode, I would need treatment fast to stop it before things escalated. Mom's kidney was fine, I was sure of it. This just couldn't be rejection.

I gave Dr G a hug goodbye at the airport and thanked him for his care and support during the Games. I could almost feel him willing me to go home with the team. But this could be my last holiday – I had missed so many in the last three years – and I needed to go and enjoy it before more hospital time.

As it turned out, the blood tests didn't improve but I continued to have a great holiday on both sides of the US. I loved San Francisco as much as Vancouver – it reminded me of Cape Town. And being in Florida was a really good chance to catch up with Kristen and her family.

However, it was soon time to face the music and I had barely unpacked before Dr G whisked me back into Frere Hospital to try and work out what the problem was. More tests and scans (I refused a biopsy) and we were still unsure what was behind my raised creatinine. Cape Town again – and off I flew.

I arrived in Cape Town and baffled the team for a few more days until they discovered that I had a PUJ (pulmonary ureteric junction) which is a bit like an obstruction in the ureter. In simple terms, this meant that Mom's ureter had a kink or blockage in it, causing the waste urine from her/my kidney, Bernie, to get stuck before it could travel to my bladder. This was causing damage to the ureter and my kidney was suffering as a result. If we didn't do something about the kink it would mean long-term damage and possible kidney failure. Again!

Strange as it may sound, this was the greatest news – because it wasn't rejection. This was fixable; rejection was more of a gamble. I didn't have to go through the trauma of huge steroidal doses like with the first transplant, which hadn't saved it anyway. And I could blame Mom for this one – for once it wasn't my body which was causing the problem, it was her kidney and ureter. Not that this made any difference of course, it still ended up being my problem.

The doctors set about the complicated task of working out what to do. It was slightly unusual and I am not sure they had seen one of these in a transplant recipient before. To avoid damaging the kidney further by having the waste fluid seep back in and poison it, they wound a tiny little tube inside my kidney which drained the urine straight out. Quite disgustingly, I was weeing out of my side!

Oh yes, it was as uncool as it could possibly get. What was worse, even after the repair had been done and they'd pulled the little tube out, the wee continued to seep out of the hole for several days. It was freaky and never have I wished for the ability to wee in a toilet more.

More surgery. This time they replaced Bernie's damaged ureter with one of my own, which was luckily still intact and connected to one of my now shrivelled-up prune-sized kidneys. The operation was a success and soon my creatinine started coming back down to a more normal level. It never did drop to the all-time low I had enjoyed just after the transplant, but it was stable and everyone was happy.

I was also so grateful that they had tried everything before just pumping me with more steroids, which is often the knee-jerk reaction to any spike in the blood tests. Most transplantation issues are to do with rejection. I had a good kidney though and, most would say, the best match possible. I had to believe this one was for life.

Dr B was one of my favourite registrars at Groote Schuur. He was younger than my consultants and still in training, so eager to learn. My case was an exciting one. In fact I attracted a lot of trainees because of the continual medical challenges I posed. I looked forward to Dr B's daily check-ups, which kept me going while I was in Groote Schuur. He had a good sense of humour and I knew he really cared. He also made me feel like a person rather than a patient when he sat and chatted to me – that is such a rarity when you are part of a hospital system. We often had good talks about life in general.

When I felt it was time, I started pushing the doctors to let me go back to East London. They knew how much I hated being so far from home, but they were ever mindful that I needed to be in easy reach of emergency help, should I require it. As usual I was always trying to leave hospital before my body was ready.

Dr B had seen me at my most pathetic and dealt with my whinging when he removed my weeing tube. He knew I was ready and desperate to get out of the confines of hospital once more. He saw that I was now reaching the end of my tether and incredibly kindly offered to take me out earlier. He said I could spend the evening with him and his girlfriend. They would drop me off at the airport the following day. He would then be able to watch over me and make sure I was strong enough to go home. Was that a good enough deal?

When I think of this gesture now, it is one of the kindest and most generous things that a doctor has done for me and once again highlights the amazing care and empathy that I received during my many months at Groote Schuur.

After packing up, we left in the early afternoon and drove around Signal Hill in Cape Town. Dr B, a passionate paraglider, wanted a little flight before heading home and he thought the fresh air would do me good. He supplied me with water and snacks and dropped me off on the rocks of Camps Bay so I could watch the waves crash into shore. He then drove up the back of Table Mountain. While I sat in the glow of the afternoon sun, I gazed up at the majestic mountain and watched him glide off the peak before floating gently down to the landing zone near where I was sitting. I decided then that I would have to add this to my bucket list. Jumping off a mountain looked incredible.

It was the perfect afternoon. After having been cooped up for so long in the sterile hospital environment, my senses were heightened and extra appreciative of the sounds of the ocean, the smells of the spray and the warm sand between my toes. Watching people walk by, I wondered at the strangeness of my situation. Here I was, a transplant patient just out of hospital, getting over my recent operation and waiting for my doctor to jump off a mountain.

*

In the year that followed the World Transplant Games my life settled into a wonderful routine of golf and part-time work at Taylors Sports. My focus included promoting organ donation and the success of transplantation. I made sure I spoke to groups whenever I could. I got involved with the local Leo Club (the youth branch of Lions International) and started to find fulfilment in charity work. Fundraising for the next World Games became a priority too and I joined the South African Transplant Games committee, increasing awareness of this amazing bi-annual world sporting event and helping our team grow and get ready for the next one.

But I was soon faced with yet another medical challenge.

I had numerous tests, but there didn't seem to be any reason for my irregular and heavy menstrual bleeding. It had gone on for so long. I kept hoping that things would settle down, but here I was buying my second box of forty tampons in a month. At this rate I would go broke from a bleeding uterus.

It was so frustrating, not to mention limiting and upsetting. I wanted to be free to enjoy my new life with Bernie. After a faulty start with a gynaecologist I would rather not mention, the lovely Dr Bowen came into my life. The minute I walked into his surgery, I knew I would be okay. He put me at ease and I trusted him immediately.

Despite lots more tests and even a biopsy (no screaming from me), nothing out of the ordinary showed up. We both thought it might be a long-term effect of the anti-rejection drugs. The first treatment we tried was a Depo-Provera contraceptive injection. It was supposed to last three months and reduce my symptoms. But this is me we are talking about. Nothing changed.

Dr Bowen then decided to try something radical. He sent me to Groote Schuur Hospital (by now my second home) to undergo a procedure to clear out the endometrium (the membrane that lines the womb). Because the procedure was new, Groote Schuur was the only place doing it. I was ready to try anything.

The transplant team were happy to see me but sorry that I was facing yet another challenge. Fiona, the transplant coordinator and my friend, was there to greet me and I spent most of my time visiting them for morning coffee after they'd completed their rounds. After all, I wasn't sick, just in for a minor procedure. But once again I was going to be undergoing something unusual. The gynaecologists had never performed this on a transplant recipient before so my transplant team were heavily involved in the preparations.

Just before I was due to go into theatre Prof Kahn popped by to check up on me and make sure I was ready.

'Helen, have you spoken to the guys about tying your tubes?'

'What? No!' I wasn't sure why he was asking.

'Well, due to the nature of what you have been through and the fact that they are going into the area anyway, I really think it would be wise to tie your tubes now. It would avoid having to do this later.'

'Does that mean you don't think I should have children?'

Prof Kahn went on to explain how risky it would be for me to fall pregnant now or at any stage in the near future. He didn't think my body would cope with a pregnancy.

I stared at him as he continued.

'Some transplant recipients have had children, but it is rare and still risky. I am sure you would not want to jeopardise your transplant.'

What could I say? Of course I didn't want to jeopardise this precious gift, but, hell, I was just twenty-four and I really hadn't given the prospect of children much thought.

The consent form was changed to reflect this new addition to the procedure and I was left to ponder my life-altering decision while they got ready to send me to surgery. I remember wondering what would happen if I fell in love with someone who wanted children and I couldn't have them. Would they leave me? I had never really contemplated the idea of having children, simply because I wasn't ready to consider a family. Not being in a steady relationship, it just hadn't entered my mind. I had always thought there would be time for that later.

These days many transplant recipients do have successful pregnancies and experience the gift of children. But I was not meant to – of that I am convinced. In the early 1990s there was much less information about it and far fewer success stories. The drugs I was taking to prevent rejection could have affected the unborn child and there was also uncertainty around breastfeeding afterwards. My kidney failure had taken its toll on my body. Bringing a child into the world would just be too hard.

The procedure went well. No more bleeding afterwards, which was great. However, they found a large polyp in my uterus. This had not been there a few weeks before when Dr Bowen had performed a biopsy so it was obviously very new and growing fast. It was removed and sent for testing. I flew back home to East London thinking nothing of it.

When the results arrived, it was bad news. The polyp was cancerous and although they were sure that they had removed all of it, the risk of leaving my uterus intact was just too great. Why I had developed this cancerous polyp was anyone's guess. It might have been because of the last few years of fighting kidney failure and the numerous drugs I had been given or it might have simply been bad luck. Either way, plans were made for me to fly back to Cape Town immediately for a hysterectomy. My uterus was close to the transplanted kidney so, even though Dr Bowen could have performed the operation, he thought it best I had it at Groote Schuur with the full transplant team around me.

This was the first time I really cried. Not because I was going to lose my uterus, but because I was just not ready for another major operation. It would be my twentieth surgical procedure in four years and I was tired. When would this end? I hated being in hospital, despised having a general anaesthetic, which made me nauseous every time, and loathed the painful drips, the stitches and even the recovery time. Everything about surgery sucked!

I flew back to Cape Town (frequent flyer points would have been good to collect over the last four years) and this time had enlisted the help of a former schoolfriend. No one else was free to pick me up so Paul was my wingman for this little experience. Poor guy – he had been my high-school maths tutor and schoolgirl crush, but I don't think he expected at twenty-four to be my escort to hospital for a hysterectomy. He was funny and intelligent and we had lots of good conversations about the philosophy of life. He was totally unfazed by it all and was happy to help.

After a night with Paul's family at their gorgeous cliff-side home overlooking Camps Bay, I found myself back at Groote Schuur. This time I was on a new floor, in the Cancer Ward. How depressing. To make matters worse, it was virtually underground, dark and quiet and with no view. I was surrounded by lots of older and much sicker patients. Fortunately I was put in a private ward (being friends with the Head Matron had its perks) and I set up home for another extended stay.

I loved my new doctor, another specialist registrar. He was young and friendly and we had lots of fun joking together. I looked forward to his daily rounds, which were a highlight in the otherwise tedious hospital routine. Meals were a way of breaking up the day too, though, just like on long-haul flights, you wait impatiently for them but actually never like the food.

My hysterectomy went very well and I need not have worried about stitches. The surgeons went one step further this time and used a zip plaster. Incredible! There was no pain or pulling after the surgery and there were absolutely no stitches whatsoever. Surgical heaven. If I could have, I would have sold those zip plasters around the world – they were my kind of product.

Apart from a wound infection (one of the risks of the zip), everything went really well and I was back home after a month. It was a long month. However, I was feeling incredibly positive about looking forward again. The actual repercussions of the hysterectomy were of little consequence because I knew this was out of my hands. Children had not been a consideration before and my future was hard to imagine anyway, let alone one that included motherhood. In the last few years I had become used to living one day at a time. There was nothing to hold me back now. It felt like I had turned a corner. Four years was enough. It was time to start living and time to see the world.

16
An Adventurous Spirit

'Go after your dream, no matter how unattainable others think it is.'

— Linda Mastandrea

began to look for my next adventure. East London was feeling constricting. Everywhere I went, people knew me and I was finding it hard to shake the label of 'kidney kid'. As much as this close-knit community had helped me get through the last four years of hell, I felt that it was not the place I was meant to be. Twenty surgeries, hundreds of needles and many challenging months in hospital had changed me. I wanted to spread my wings and fly. It was time to leave the safe haven of my family home and explore the world once more.

It was going to be difficult to leave my friends, but people move on and you really need to do what is right for you in order to follow your dreams. I am sure it was hard for my parents to let me go. My sister was about to leave too and experience life in England with my Aunt Jen, so it was just going to be me and Pete at home. I think he was probably relieved to see me go – the drama was tedious.

I was still involved with the Transplant Games Association in South Africa and the next World Games were to be in Manchester in 1995, around nine months away. It would be the perfect catalyst for getting me overseas again. I had done it before. I could do it again. It was time to get training.

I set about raising funds for my trip and getting fitter and stronger. I needed to get back on the golf course fast. Christmas was approaching so I decided to make mini Christmas cakes to sell at the local Christmas fairs and open houses. I'm not sure why I thought baking would work, but it was easy to do because it required little physical effort except mixing and decorating. Using my grandma's recipe and recycled tuna tins, I baked hundreds of cakes. And I mean hundreds! The house became a makeshift bakery. The cakes made perfect gifts for teachers, friends and families and I started a roaring trade.

Many late evenings were spent with the family who all helped me with cake-decorating. Each tuna tin-sized Christmas cake was iced, tied with tartan ribbon, decorated with Christmas holly or stamps and then wrapped in cellophane. It was fiddly work but they looked beautiful when completed. Despite being restricted by no heavy lifting and no driving, friends and family helped me make the sales and get the cakes out in time.

Making hundreds of Christmas cakes helped me raise funds to travel to the Games

I met my hero, Dr Christiaan Barnard, who performed the first heart transplant at Groote Schuur, at the Manchester Games in 1995.

EL trio selected for unusual honour

by JAN HENNOP

FIGHTING FIT: The three transplant patients chosen to represent South Africa in the World Transplant Games in England, Mr Rob Stone, at the back, Mr Teddy Betchoo, and Helen Philpott with Frere Hospital's, Sister Joan McMillan, centre.

EAST LONDON — Three East London kidney transplant patients have been chosen as members of a team to represent South Africa in the World Transplant Games in Manchester next month.

Miss Helen Philpott, Mr Rob Stone and Mr Teddy Betchoo, who had transplants in 1992 and 1993, will have the chance to strut their stuff at the games with 23 other South Africans, competing in various track and field events.

Miss Philpott said yesterday the aim of the games was to show that people could participate in sport after having a life threatening operation.

"We have been given a second chance, and the games really give us something to work towards. It also gives us the chance to meet new friends and experience great camaraderie," she said.

A previous gold medalist at the games in Vancouver, Canada in 1993, Miss Philpott will represent the country on the golf course, while Mr Stone will participate in the swimming events. Mr Betchoo is the sprint specialist, participating in the 100 m and 200 m track events.

Mr Stone, a former Border surfer, said he would return to the waves after the games.

As far as South Africa's chances were concerned, the three were equally optimistic.

"We have won a couple of medals at the previous games, and we are definitely going to try to improve on our last performance," Miss Philpott said.

Travelling with the team will be Mrs Joan McMillan, of Frere Hospital's renal unit, who encouraged all three of the competitors throughout their illnesses and helped them after their transplants.

"Joan has been a help to us all along and will be travelling with us to give us support," Mr Betchoo said.

Credit: East London Daily Dispatch

165

This, together with income from my hours at Taylors, from teaching cross-stitching at Clarendon Primary School and being secretary of the Border Tennis Association, meant I was able to save enough money to travel overseas and join the South African team in Manchester the following year.

It was great to have the focus of the Games to get me back on my feet for a second time and shake off my last major operation. Arriving in Manchester was like being at a reunion. It was such fun to see everyone again and meet up with old transplant friends from around the world. We had sadly lost a few friends in the two years since Vancouver, but all in all it was a fantastic week. The highlight was another gold medal and a closing party at the Granada Film studios.

I made a special new golfing friend that year: Kyle, a young American who had received a liver transplant a year before. We stayed in touch for many years, meeting up at the various Games every two years. Sadly, Kyle died from a blood infection, just a year after he married the love of his life, leaving behind a little daughter. It was such a shame after fifteen fabulous years with his new liver, and a sobering reminder of how fleeting life can be. He was only thirty when he died.

After the Games, my sister Michelle and I set off on a long-planned trip to Europe. I had wanted to do this before my kidneys failed. Mich had been living with our Aunt Jenny in Bridlington, a small seaside town in Yorkshire, and saving her wages while working at the local pub. Jen was such a huge support for all of us, and over the years myself as well and Pete and Mich all spent time in Bridlington with her. She was there whenever we needed her.

I felt confident travelling with Michelle. She knew me well and understood my health issues. It would be less complicated than doing such a long trip with friends. Being three years post transplant, there were few risks to travelling now. The main concern was ensuring I had contingency plans ready in case something were to go wrong or if I was to fall ill. Because my dad was born in the UK, I too had a British passport, which meant that I could get medical treatment in Europe if I needed it. We just made sure that I had at least double the amount of medication I expected to use so that if we lost any on the way we had back-up. I was on three-monthly blood testing now, so I scheduled my last test close to our departure date and another for just after our return.

Michelle was designated train-time checker and I was tour guide. We bought a Euro rail ticket, which allowed us to travel by train to pretty much anywhere in Europe, stopping wherever and whenever we wanted. We had a rough idea of where we could go, but basically our plan was to just choose a country and then find a good train to get us there. This was our way of living on the edge!

Our ferry from Hull took us to Bruges in Belgium where our adventure began. Neither of was especially good at packing light. Luckily we were similar sizes so we shared jeans (five pairs!) and plenty of tops, shorts and shoes. Way too much for backpacking. Mich had a backpack. I used a kitbag – what was I thinking? The only arguments we had were about clothes and who should wear which outfit on what day. Neither of us was good on decision-making but we managed.

We had a fantastic adventure and it was an experience neither of us will forget. Our travels took us to eleven countries in five weeks. Through various family connections and friendships we knew someone in nearly every country on our list and had somewhere to stay everywhere except Poland and France. Whenever possible we did our train journeys at night, saving daytimes for sightseeing. Food was a mix of crackers, baguettes, peanut butter and Nutella. When we stayed with friends they treated us to traditional home-cooked meals and we made sure we ate pizza in Italy, cheese in the Netherlands, baguettes in France and chocolate in Switzerland.

We had just a few hairy moments when we were nearly robbed on a train and got lost in Marseille (the map we had just didn't extend as far as our hostel). However, we mostly had an amazing experience and adopted a number of friends along the way. In Italy we fell in love with Rome and Venice. We celebrated my twenty-fifth birthday in Milan with my dear friend Jackie who had moved over for work. We did the impractical and bought Venetian crystal wine glasses in Venice for Dad to spoil him on his forthcoming fiftieth – it proved quite a challenge to backpack with six large and delicate wine glasses. Naive but thoughtful was our excuse.

In Switzerland we were hosted by friends in villages near Zermatt in the west and St Moritz on the east. The valley views were absolutely stunning and waking to the sound of cow bells was a unique experience. Germany was another wonderful treat. Mich and I spent a glorious few days in Stuttgart and enjoyed a tour of the famous Mercedes Benz factory thanks to our friend who worked there. Budapest, Vienna and Prague featured on our tour. We even went to Bratislava, staying with our acupuncturist's mother. Her lack of English meant Mich was given vodka for breakfast. Serves her right for having said how much she liked it the night before!

Travelling around Europe was another dream come true for me. The memories Michelle and I have from that trip are special and lasting. It meant a lot that she was willing to share this adventure with me and I was grateful to have had the opportunity. She gave me the strength and the confidence to do it and I am so pleased we did.

*

After our tour around Europe I went home to South Africa to spend Christmas with the rest of the family. Finding my way was becoming increasingly hard. I had huge gaps in my CV and I really wasn't sure what I should be doing with this gift of a second chance in life. As much as I was positive, determined, happy and willing to try anything, I was still feeling lost and unsure of my future.

The sun was glistening on the water as I lay on the lilo. Our back garden in East London was idyllic, the perfect place to relax. My idea of heaven. In the distance I heard the phone ring.

'Helen, it's for you!' shouted my brother.

I scrambled out of the water and wrapped a towel around me before heading inside to pick up the phone.

'Hello, cuz, how are you?' It was my cousin by marriage, who lived in the UK.

'Dave! How great to hear from you! What's up?'

'Oh, I just wanted to find out what you are doing right now.'

'Right now? Well, lying in the pool and soaking up this summer sun. It's a hard life, you know.' I suddenly had a thought. 'It must be freezing over there?'

'It sure is. But listen, I have a job for you. Can you cook?

Cook? Of course I could cook.

He went on. 'How would you like to join me in France? I could really do with your help.'

'France? Seriously? What job?'

'I need another chalet girl. It means cooking, cleaning and looking after the chalet guests in Méribel. During your spare time you can ski. Do you think you could get a flight next week?'

I had never skied before. Never been to the mountains and didn't speak a word of French. Could I do this? Why not!

It was one of the most exciting experiences of my life. I spent four months in France, enjoying skiing in the famous three valleys of Courchevel, Méribel and Val Thorens, as well as on the slopes of Val d'Isère and Tignes.

My first proper ski was down a blue run in Tignes with absolutely no idea of what I was doing. The run took me two hours to master and after a hot chocolate laced with rum I was back up and building in confidence. By the end of the season, my skiing was above average and I was soon whizzing down all runs including the gruelling Méribel blacks.

I had never imagined I would be fortunate enough to enjoy the white stuff and live on the edge like that. Skiing has become an annual holiday now and I love heading off to the slopes with family and friends. I have even suffered the bruising but exhilarating joy of learning how to snowboard. The snow has become one of my favourite places to be.

In Monte Carlo with my sister Michelle

17
A Life Purpose

'Your time is limited, so don't waste it living someone else's life. Don't be trapped by dogma – which is living with the results of other people's thinking. Don't let the noise of others' opinions drown out your own inner voice. And most important, have the courage to follow your heart and intuition. They somehow already know what you truly want to become. Everything else is secondary.'

– Steve Jobs

Europe gave me the travelling bug and after another Christmas in South Africa I left for Australia. I set up home in Sydney and was quickly seduced by its stunning setting and the laid-back lifestyle Australians are so good at creating. Living there was fabulous and I ended up staying for four years. I felt totally at home and made some wonderful friends. My health was in good shape: I was still stable, kidney function was excellent and my previous medical issues felt like they belonged to someone else. It was great to start over in such a beautiful place. I even fell in love for the first time. I found someone I thought was my soulmate and for a short while it was fantastic. Although it came to a tumultuous end, I found peace with the fact that he wasn't meant to be 'the one'. But that wasn't the big story of my time in Australia. The really important thing that happened down under was that I discovered my life purpose.

It was June 1997 and I'd been in Australia for about three months. I was working with Mark Cox promoting the World Transplant Games and we had a stand at a Transplant Conference at Darling Harbour in Sydney. The event was buzzing. There were so many specialists and medical teams from around the world and during the breaks between talks they flocked around the stalls area enjoying coffee and cake. My stand, which was in a prominent spot, was getting lots of visitors. One of them was a tall, white-haired man who introduced himself as Doug from the Australian Kidney Foundation.

I was intrigued to learn more about this kidney charity and find out how I could get involved. My mission was to promote kidney health awareness and organ donation wherever I could, and I already had experience with the Border Kidney Association and the national Transplant Games Association in South Africa. I got so much out of my work as a volunteer and I can't recommend it enough: whether you have health problems or not, there is nothing more motivating than doing something that makes a difference in the world.

By the end of my chat with Doug I had convinced him that he needed someone like me on his team and had sold him all my ideas for raising awareness about and fundraising for the Australian Kidney Foundation. The following week was National Kidney Awareness Week and he asked me to join him at a campaigning event at a nearby shopping centre. A week after that, Doug employed me – for a proper salary – to coordinate support groups, educate the public about kidney health and raise funds via the numerous events and activities that were happening around New South Wales.

This was my big break and I made the job my own. Soon I was growing teams of volunteers and developing close working partnerships with the Red Cross Organ Donation team. Together we promoted the benefits of transplantation and raised awareness of the desperate need for organs. There were many people waiting for transplants in Australia. I became the spokesperson for the Australian Kidney Foundation in Sydney, which later became known as Kidney Health Australia. It was a hugely fulfilling role and it made me realise that doing a job you love means that it will never feel like work. I learnt that you have to try and choose something that fuels your passion; doing so keeps you motivated and helps you achieve your life ambitions. I am forever grateful to Doug for believing in me and giving me the opportunity to build my charity experience.

Kidney woman to help Aussies

By Tiana Stevens

EAST LONDON — Kidney recipient and sportswoman Helen Philpott is leaving East London next weekend for Sydney to work for Australian Kidney Foundation.

Helen's story touched the hearts of many people in 1992 when her mother, Mrs Bernadine Philpott, donated a kidney to save her life as well as her promising sporting career.

Helen later went on to excel at golf. A year later, she collected a gold medal in the ninth World Transplant Games in Vancouver. Back in East London for the past two weeks, Helen has been spending time with family and friends before jetting off on a "challenging adventure" for four years.

"I feel I can do a lot of work in Sydney, this opportunity has opened up many doors for me to continue the work I love," she said.

Having just returned from Australia in March, Helen spent a year as an education and promotions officer for the Australian Kidney Foundation.

After falling in love with the bright lights of Sydney, the sunny weather and the friendly people, Helen is adamant she will see more of the country on this trip. While travelling, she hopes to combine sightseeing with educating people about her experience and the warning signs of kidney failure.

"This is fulfilling work to talk to people and educate them on transplants and the trauma it causes",

she said.

After winning gold in the Sydney World Transplant Games last year, Helen has been attempting to write a book on her experiences as a kidney recipient.

"Because you write the pages over and over again, the book takes time to write, and to make it perfect in the way I want it," Helen said.

"I have to relive the experience all over again each time I sit down to write and that is hard for me."

Helen believes the Sydney Transplant Games last year had such a positive effect on her, with it being the first time donor family members could become involved that "I can't wait to go back to Australia and get involved again."

Credit: East London Daily Dispatch

The South African team at the World Transplant Games in Sydney in 1997.
I won gold for golf. I'm second from the right at the bottom.

173

My friend Lisa (a bone marrow transplant recipient) and I ran the City to Surf in Sydney in support of transplantation awareness.

Public speaking became one of my main tasks and I gave talks regularly, sometimes two or three times a week, to various organisations, schools, companies and community groups. Anyone who wanted to learn more about kidney disease or find out about organ donation was referred to me. Because of the scale of the job and the size of New South Wales, I decided to train other transplant recipients and empower them to share their story too.

I was given media and public speaking training to prepare me for the numerous talks to camera, interviews on the radio and quotes for newspapers. I learnt how to use body language effectively, manage my nerves and avoid difficult questions by focusing on the message that I wanted to share. I was already quite a gutsy and articulate twenty-seven-year-old but training taught me to engage the audience so that they really heard and understood my message. I loved to talk, but I learnt to love my audience more.

The power that I had to influence and empower people to change was intoxicating. There was so much I wanted to tell the world and every talk gave me a chance to educate the public about the value of kidneys and how important it is to make a decision about organ donation. I knew it was a privilege to be given just five minutes with an audience. In order to make those five minutes count, I wanted to be the best speaker I could. Learning to breathe, use my tone of voice and eye contact and develop a natural conversational style that was unique to me was all part of my growth and development as a speaker. I've valued the insights and learning ever since and use them to this day in my work as a public speaker.

One of my most memorable tasks was when media tycoon Kerry Packer – the owner of various Australian newspapers and TV stations at the time – received a kidney from his helicopter pilot. Not only was Kerry Packer extremely high-profile but his life-saving transplant was made possible by a donor who was not related to him. This broke new ground. At that time most living donors were either related or married to the recipient; receiving a kidney from a colleague or employee was new. It opened up a whole new debate.

Obviously no one in the family was keen to do media interviews and so it was me they called. I had never met Kerry Packer or his family, but my role at the AKF and my experience of transplantation meant I was well placed to comment. I saw the headlines in the *Sydney Morning Herald* while enjoying my Manly ferry ride to work that morning. The calls from radio and TV stations started soon afterwards.

I learnt to love the media and being readily available helped them get the stories they needed. If we were having success in educating Australians about the issues of kidney health and organ donation then I was happy to talk.

As part of my role, I helped organise the annual Kidney Kids Camp, which was for children who were on dialysis or had had a life-saving transplant. We secured the best view on Sydney Harbour for a select group of these Kidney Kids to enjoy the new millennium fireworks – at none other than the Governor General's House, right opposite the famous Sydney Opera House. The kids 'camped' in the Governor General's lounge and I slept under the dining room table along with the rest of the adult support team on the day. The Prime Minister, John Howard, wandered over from his home next door to greet us all and have a chat to the kids while we enjoyed the magnificent spectacle. It was a very special night.

The Prime Minister and the Governor General of Australia celebrating the new millennium with Kidney Kids on Sydney Harbour.

Me and the Governor General of Australia

Doug ensured that I was sponsored so that I could continue to live in Australia and I stayed for four years at the AKF. Living in Manly, in Sydney's Northern Beaches, was wonderful and although I moved quite a few times, my last flat there was with my friend Val. She had also benefited from a successful kidney transplantation and we had an instant connection and close friendship.

Manly provided a wonderful backdrop for evening powerwalks, early-morning swims at the pool, lazy breakfasts at my favourite café, boogie-boarding in the waves and rollerblading along the beach front. I fell in love with the Aussie latte. It became my staple drink and I had my favourite barista who prepared it just the way I liked.

Australia was made even better because of my friends. They were my family and provided me with such happiness and support. We shared many adventures, holidays, nights out and parties, one of them being my thirtieth birthday. It makes for an interesting night when you invite plenty of boys but not many girls and mix that with cocktails and dancing. Celebrating the milestone of turning thirty was special. Ten years before, I would never have believed it possible.

Wonderful Sydney

*

All the time I was in Australia I continued to take my golf seriously. I played whenever I could with friends and spent hours at the driving range in Narrabeen, just north of Manly. I relished being in a climate not so dissimilar from South Africa's: it was rarely too wet or cold to go out and play, even in the winter months.

I became increasingly tempted by the notion of trying to become the first professional golfer with a kidney transplant. To do so would require relocating to the UK. Eventually I decided it was now or never, so, four years after joining AKF, I downed my last Aussie latte and headed for Europe.

By this stage my mom and dad had moved to England. They'd left South Africa in 2000, principally because they wanted to be near my brother and sister, who were both living in the UK. So in May 2001 I found myself living with my parents in Epsom, Surrey. And spending a huge amount of time on the golf course. The English weather was a shock, even more so out on the links. I had arrived in spring but it was still cool and frost glistened on the grass every morning. However, I was no stranger to discipline, motivation and overcoming adversity and simply put on an extra couple of layers to combat the cold wind on the driving range

I was so sure that playing professional golf would be one of my life achievements. It felt good to be out on the course, and hitting that little white ball gave me such pleasure. But moving back to the UK to live with my parents was never going to be easy. I had lived in Australia for four years, was hugely independent and used to an outdoor, beach lifestyle. Plus just going out on tour would not be that simple. I had to get my handicap right down to low single figures or, ideally, scratch (zero) and develop my game so that I had a chance with the best. I decided that I should find work for the moment and continue practising until I was able to play fulltime.

After being bridesmaid at my sister's wedding, I landed a job at a local PR agency, which allowed me to work during the day and continue practising in the evenings. It was light until 10 p.m. so it gave me more than enough daylight hours to fit in the driving range and the odd game with Dad or Michelle.

The job was interesting and the people I worked with were good fun. I learnt a lot about the public relations industry but soon realised that I was not cut out for the 'Sweetie! Darling!' role and we parted ways. I suffered through a few temping roles both locally in Epsom and then later in London. All just paid the bills and kept me on the golf course when I could play. Winter was tough. It really was impossible to play sometimes and I had to be content with just undercover range practice or fitness training.

Finally I secured a job with the local branch of a chain of professional golf shops, on a course about half an hour from East

Grinstead, where Mom, Dad and I were now living. It was so exciting to be in the golfing environment at last and to feel one step closer to realising my dream.

Working in the pro shop was just like working at Taylors Sports. The young guys who were also dreaming of a professional career were great golfers, good fun and as usual more interested in playing golf than doing any work. I really struggled to cope with the low salary, which was just above minimum wage, and had to supplement my income with pub work in our local village. This meant less time for golf and I found I was working in the golf industry but not actually playing much at all.

Then I met Glen. He strolled into the shop one day doing one of the deliveries from head office. He was a golf professional, working part-time managing all the stock in the chain's shops and playing tournaments the rest of the time. I was immediately drawn to him – he was Australian!

'It is so nice to meet you,' I gushed. 'I'm Helen.'

He smiled and said hello in a deep Australian drawl.

I rushed straight on to tell him that I had recently returned from wonderful Australia and was trying to become a golfer. He was surprised that I had come back to the UK for golf – considering the challenging weather.

'Well, my visa was not going to last so I had to leave,' I explained. 'In fact, what I need is an Australian to marry me and then I can go back. You wouldn't consider it?'

It was worth a shot. I was starting to regret my haste at leaving God's Own Country.

Over the weeks I chatted more to Glen. He gave me the harsh truth about what it would take to become a professional: hit at least 300 golf balls a day! Hmm, maybe I wasn't cut out for that sort of profession. No way was I doing that in sub-zero temperatures.

It didn't take long for me to realise that I wasn't going to make it as a professional golfer. The lack of finances was a real struggle. I was so used to eating out, spending time with friends, travelling, shopping and so forth that suddenly having to spend what little I had on golf balls at the range or membership at a club was making me feel too restricted. Plus I really wasn't enjoying the hours of practice in solitude, and the weather was extremely hard for me to handle. I hate the cold. Swinging a club when you are dressed as a Michelin man was not my idea of fun.

I started looking for other opportunities and stumbled across an advert in the paper for a job in Fuerteventura, one of the Canary Islands. It was a sales job, it was somewhere warm and it was an island. Why not?

On my last day at the golf shop, Glen rang and asked to speak to me. He said that he wanted to say goodbye and wish me well. He was also sorry we hadn't had a game of golf yet. This was a surprise to me. I was sure he thought I was a complete crazy.

'Well, how about a game before I leave then?' I asked.

'If you have the time, that would be great!'

We had a really good game together. Glen was easy to talk to and interesting. I was intrigued and decided that I really liked him. Our game over, we spent hours in the clubhouse until I had to drag myself home to finish packing. We promised to stay in touch. I had the feeling that I might be making a mistake leaving this guy behind – there was something about him.

I lasted three weeks in Fuerteventura. The job was not what I expected and I didn't approve of the manipulative sales procedure we had to follow to try and sell the holiday club on the island.

Glen and I emailed as often as possible and I couldn't wait to get to the internet café every day to check my messages. I soon realised that I was on the wrong island and flew home to Britain.

It took Glen and me many more games of golf before I demanded that he take me out on a real date without any clubs in sight. Eventually we got married, bought a house and started our lives together in East Grinstead. Jasper, the cutest Jack Russell, made our little family complete

As for my dream of becoming a professional golfer, I was again reminded of what I'd learnt at the AKF in Sydney: to stay motivated you need to love what you do. And that made me dive right back into the charity world again.

My special little family

Our special wedding day on 22nd July 2005.

18
Making a Difference

'Learn from the Starfish Story - you too can make a difference in this world! Continue to set goals and strive to achieve them.'
— Mike and Bernadine Philpott

Over the next decade I took on a series of extremely rewarding jobs in the charity sector. At Kidney Research UK I established and helped grow the London Bridges Walk. What started as a walk across five of London's bridges, with 120 people raising £12,000 in the first year, developed into an annual event with more than 1,500 participants walking across eight of London's famous bridges and raising well over £150,000 annually. It has grown even bigger since.

As the recipient of one of the first live-donor transplants in South Africa, I know only too well what a privilege it is to receive brand-new, cutting-edge treatment. Without vital research into the causes of kidney failure and the way in which this complex condition is treated, nothing will change. Charities like Kidney Research UK make sure that the advances in treatments keep on coming. On that first Bridges Walk, when we saw the sea of purple T-shirts snake along the Thames and the smiles on everyone's faces, we knew we were helping people give to a cause they believed in. I was really proud of the difference we were able to make to others going through the trauma of kidney failure.

People come into your life for a reason, a season or a lifetime. I have learnt to understand the difference and to cherish every significant relationship, whatever its duration. In my next charity role, at Teenage Cancer Trust, I was to encounter two extraordinary people, in quite different capacities.

The first of those was the fundraising manager who hired me to work at the charity. Heather was a huge bundle of energy, ideas, enthusiasm and passion and she taught me everything I needed to know about launching and running major capital appeals. Having a mentor really lifted my confidence and helped me excel in the role. When I joined, in 2007, Teenage Cancer Trust had just twenty-five staff members; by the time I left five years later it had grown to around 150. For me, working to try and make a difference for teenagers with cancer was of great personal significance. Part of that was having been a teenager myself with a chronic, life-threatening illness. I could empathise with them and had a sense of what it's like to have your life and future in the balance. I had got away relatively lightly: the cancerous polyp on my womb had been removed in the hysterectomy operation I'd had at twenty-four and very fortunately I'd had no recurrence. Many other teenagers have a far worse time of it.

From a career point of view, I was excited about having the opportunity both to establish the charity's presence in the south-east of England and to raise funds for specialist units. These would ensure young people had the best possible experience in hospital while undergoing treatment. Raising funds had become my passion. I was good at it. I will never forget one of my managers saying to me, 'Helen, you have an incredible skill for fundraising. If I dropped you in a desert, I know you would find a way to raise funds.'

What I love about fundraising is that it is all about people and the relationships you have with them. Heather always used to say, 'People buy from people.' It was so true. Success is based on how much your supporters know, like and trust you. Classic marketing. Over the years I have met the most amazingly generous, kind and thoughtful donors and all because they were touched and moved to give to the various causes I was passionately trying to get vital support for. My work in the Major Donor arena was particularly fun and I loved having a window into the world of the rich, the famous and the philanthropic.

During my time at Teenage Cancer Trust I ran two multi-million-pound capital appeals. These fundraising campaigns took me across the south-east of England as well as to the wonderful Channel Islands. I made many fruitful visits to both Guernsey and Jersey, helping increase awareness of teenage cancer and raise funds for units where local children would be treated.

Louise, Anna and me celebrating the opening of the new Teenage Cancer Trust unit at the Royal Marsden in Surrey after our fundraising efforts.

As part of a 'Blue Day' campaign to raise funds for teenagers with cancer, the celebrity chef from Jersey, Shaun Rankin and I delivered over 2,000 blue cupcakes to Jersey and Guernsey businesses. We enlisted the help of Blue Islands to fly between the islands. It was a fabulous day.

It was during our fundraising campaign for the Royal Marsden unit in Sutton on the outskirts of London that I met the inspirational and incredible Nicole Dryburgh. She first contacted me in an eloquently written email, typed in a pink, asking to meet up and discuss fundraising ideas.

When I arrived, Nicole was sitting calmly on the sofa flanked by her two beloved dogs. She was slight, beautiful and had a ready smile. My shock at discovering she was not only blind, but almost totally deaf and confined to a wheelchair was soon overcome by awe at this determined young woman who wanted to make a difference to other teenagers with cancer.

Her mum 'translated' what I was saying using dead-blind sign language and soon we were giggling over chocolate cake and tea – two of our favourite shared pleasures. Soon after meeting Nicole, I learnt how to use deaf-blind sign language too so that I could communicate with Nicole myself.

Nicole soon became my most dedicated volunteer. She engaged with so many people online and successfully organised a charity ball. None of her disabilities held her back. She even wrote two books in which she shared her experience of living with cancer and the lessons she had learnt along the way: The Way I See It and Talk to the Hand. Both great reads and an incredible achievement for someone so young and for an author who couldn't see or hear.

Nicole had been diagnosed with cancer at the age of eleven. Chemotherapy, radiotherapy as well as surgery managed to put her in remission, but a brain haemorrhage caused her to go blind as a teenager. Her mother gave up work to became her primary carer and, with help from Nicole's older brother Lee, they managed well. Nicole fought cancer three times, each time overcoming the disease. Her deafness was caused by benign tumours in her ears – an unfortunate twist of fate.

Nicole and her family at Downing Street for the launch of Nicole's Fund.

Me outside No.11 Downing Street before the launch of Nicole's Fund.

Nicole giving her speech and answering questions with her Mom's help, using sign language

It didn't take me long to realise that Nicole would make an excellent fundraiser and I recruited her into my team. She touched everyone's hearts and became a very special member of our Teenage Cancer Trust family. Together we set up Nicole's Fund to raise £100,000 for the new Teenage Cancer Trust Unit at the Royal Marsden Hospital. We launched the fund at Number 11 Downing Street and Nicole proceeded to smash her target, bringing in more than £150,000.

Nicole had a bucket list. One of her wishes was to 'wobble on the cobbles' on the set of the popular soap *Coronation Street* in Manchester. Jackie didn't drive long distances, so I offered to take them both up there for a few days. It was such an eye-opener travelling with a wheelchair. Going to the toilet was a mission, as was trying to get in and out of buildings, catching a cab or just crossing the road. It soon became evident that there is a huge lack of support for anyone who relies on a wheelchair to get about. Nonetheless, Nicole did get to wobble on the cobbles and we all enjoyed our wonderful few days away.

A month later I was devastated to receive a call from Jackie telling me that Nicole had died. A massive brain haemorrhage had ended her life at twenty-two. In her short time on earth, Nicole inspired so many and made a huge difference. People still read and gain inspiration from her books. The funds she raised for both Teenage Cancer Trust and the Children's Head Trauma Unit are a lasting legacy. Nicole was funny, bright, warm and intelligent. It was an honour to have known her for a short while.

*

Running a marathon is a really popular way to raise funds and awareness for a favourite cause. It was not on my bucket list, but that had never stopped me from encouraging others to take on this huge physical challenge for charity. At Teenage Cancer Trust we were given the opportunity to apply to be the Brighton Marathon's national charity for 2011. We put in a strong application. So did many others and I knew how hard it was to get selected as charity of the year. I casually stated to the team that if we were chosen, I would run the marathon myself.

While I was lying hooked up to a drip in a hospital bed in Turkey a few months later – I had developed an acute but serious urinary tract infection which took hold just as Glen and I had started our holiday – I got a call on my mobile from Nick at the office.

'Better get those running shoes and start training!'

We had done it! Teenage Cancer Trust was the chosen charity for the event. There was no way I could back out now – I was running a marathon!

Glen decided he couldn't let me run alone so he signed up too. He was going to run in memory of our dear departed friend Nicole. We bought new running shoes and began pounding the streets around our village in September. Eight months later, after weekly training on hills, in towns and villages and along the beach in one of the coldest winters I could remember, we stood at the start line in Brighton with 13,000 other dedicated runners.

Brighton Marathon

Glen, me and Michelle at the start of the marathon.

The training was an enormous challenge. Not only was I running in near freezing conditions for the first time in my life, but my body was using muscles that had been dormant for twenty years. My training runs with Dad were a distant memory. Trying to eat enough to maintain energy was hard but a good problem to have and I enjoyed feeling fitter and leaner. Glen and I still wonder how we managed to fit the training in around our busy work schedule. Jasper definitely got fitter too and he even managed a ten-mile run on a few occasions. For a Jack Russell, that was a long way.

I tried everything to get out of the marathon. Convinced this couldn't be good for a kidney transplant recipient, I quizzed my specialists endlessly, but to no avail. They just wished me luck. My niggling injuries were also taken care of by various massage therapists and physiotherapists.

Running twenty-six miles in a day was one of the hardest things I have ever done. It was a beautiful day, sunny and warm, just the way I like it. My sister Michelle was an absolute star and cycled the entire way, cheering me on and feeding me Jelly babies and bottles of Game to keep my energy up. Glen and I crossed paths a few times en route, but mostly it was a long run by ourselves.

Crowds lined the route and we had the sea to inspire us all the way. Unfortunately, I pulled my Achilles tendon at the eight-mile mark, which made the remaining eighteen miles torturous. However, I was determined to finish the marathon, despite the growing pain in my legs, hips, knees and back. Getting over the finish line was pure relief from the longest six hours of my life.

Between us, Glen and I raised a few thousand pounds for Teenage Cancer Trust. I proved to myself and others that despite having a kidney transplant and being on long-term medication, a marathon is possible and achievable. But never again!

*

Having successfully completed two fundraising appeals for Teenage Cancer Trust – and got over the finish line of the Brighton Marathon – I needed a new challenge. It was time to take the brave leap into running my own business. Lots of people commented on what a bad time it was to set up a new venture – it was 2012 and we were deep in a recession – but I was not concerned. It felt like the best time.

My consulting business was born with the idea that I could consult for a variety of small charities and focus on my love of public speaking. Combining both my passions was exciting and scary at the same time. I particularly loved the idea of being my own boss.

I completed a coaching diploma and developed a programme of public-speaking training and coaching. At the same time I secured a long-term charity client that focused on rescuing women and children from human trafficking and slavery. The cause was such an eye-opener and a complete change to anything I had fundraised for before.

Establishing and growing my business has been both rewarding and fun. It took a while to work out that my public speaking skills could be used to inspire others to live their life in a better way and, more excitingly, empower others to speak more effectively. I am so fortunate to have the support and encouragement of my husband.

We both allow ourselves to follow our dreams – for him as a professional golfer, for me as a successful businesswoman making an impact on the world.

Public speaking is still one of the things people fear most. My challenge is to help them overcome their anxiety and learn to love speaking and sharing their message. As a qualified coach and NLP Master Practitioner, I am able to draw on this training as well as my years of speaking experience to teach others how to find their unique voice.

My advice to anyone thinking about starting a business is: just do it! There is never going to be the perfect economic climate, so make sure you follow your heart, be sensible about your goals and market like crazy when you know what you are selling and who is going to benefit from your offer. It is such a rewarding and fulfilling thing to do.

My favourite thing to do - speak!

Mom loved 'Ready, Steady, Cook' and so I convinced the producers that we needed to be on it to celebrate the 10th anniversary of the kidney transplant. It was such fun, if not a little embarrassing as I flipped pancakes on national television. She won the bake off!

19
The Bonus Years

'Twenty years from now you will be more disappointed by the things you didn't do than by the ones you did. So throw off the bowlines. Sail away from the safe harbour. Catch the wind in your sails. Explore. Dream. Discover.'

– Mark Twain

Immunosuppression is not straightforward. The organ you receive in a transplant operation is considered by your body to be a foreign object, like a splinter. When you have a splinter and don't remove it, the wound becomes infected. The same thing happens to a transplanted kidney, heart, liver, pancreas, small intestine or whatever other organ you are fortunate enough to receive. Your body tries to reject it – no matter how good the match is to your genetic DNA. The only exception seems to be in the case of identical twins.

There are many transplant anti-rejection drugs on the market today, but when I had my transplant, the choice was limited to just three. Most transplant recipients were put on all three drugs, to increase the chances of success. Every immunosuppressant drug works in a different way, blocking the T-cells or white cell development at different points along the chain of rejection. I am not a scientist so I won't try and explain the process of rejection or immunosuppression in great detail, but suffice to say it rules your life from the moment you have a transplant. Every blood test, scan and medical check-up is based around how your kidney is functioning and how happy it is in your body. As transplant recipients we live for our blood results. Creatinine is still one of the best ways to measure kidney function and rejection. No matter how many years it's been since the transplant, my stomach still turns when I make the call a few hours after the appointment to get my results. Getting a good number is such a relief.

Finding a donor is hard — there are thousands of people waiting for organs all around the world. Transplantation surgery is complicated but the surgeons have got it down to a fine art. So the biggest hurdle to successful transplantation in the long run is the drug regime and managing the complicated cocktail — too much and you damage the organ, too little and you reject it. Anti-rejection medication comes with many side effects and this the most challenging part of living with a new organ. It can increase the risk of cancer, reduce bone density, trigger excess hair production, stunt growth and cause muscle waste to name but a few. But I am sure all transplant recipients would say the same thing: it's still worth it.

Due to my sensitivity to the steroids and the horrendous experience I had with my first transplant and rejection, it was decided that a low dose of cyclosporin (a new and very expensive drug at the time) along with azathioprine (the oldest immunosuppressant drug) was going to be my best option. Cyclosporin has many side effects, the most well known being that it causes excess hair growth on the body. Being hairy and dark already, I was bound to struggle with this. After years of trying all sorts of hair management and removal techniques, I am now able to keep things under control.

But the cyclosporin also has a much more sinister side effect that I can't control. It is nephrotoxic — quite simply, it is kidney damaging. By 2012 I had been on the drug for twenty years. It was taking its toll.

At my check-up in the summer of 2012, the renal consultant at my local unit in Brighton looked worried.

'Helen, your creatinine is a little too high for my liking and the last few tests have shown that it is creeping up. I think we need to do something about it before it is too late.'

Oh boy. Here we go. The dreaded 'biopsy' word was going to rear its ugly head.

'I know what you are going to say. You want to do a biopsy. I am really not keen. Please can we find another way of working out what to do?'

I had visions of the last one, twenty-one years earlier in Cape Town, when Prof Swanepoel had the awful job of sticking a needle into my very atrophied first kidney transplant and sharing the news that it had rejected. I couldn't bear to go through that again. Plus I really hated biopsies. Needles for bloods were bad enough, but needles to remove tissue were just plain torture!

'Okay, well, if you won't have a biopsy I cannot accurately say if this is a rejection episode or if this is cyclosporin toxicity.'

I was convinced it was toxicity. Mom's kidney was a great match. It was happy, I knew it.

After much discussion and weighing up of the odds, we agreed on a solution. A new immunosuppressant. I was petrified. Stopping cyclosporin was like losing a close friend. Those fragrant cyclosporin pills had been with me for twenty years, morning and night.

Sirolimus – that was to be my new regime. It was a new drug, only ten years old and not widely used, but apparently effective. I was warned of the side effects, which included mouth ulcers, skin rashes and lung infections. All were potentially serious, but again fairly rare.

The first week went well. I was getting used to my once-a-day dose of sirolimus. Then I got the first side effect: a mouth ulcer, my first ever. My next challenge was eczema, but I thought little of it because I had experienced this before.

Blood results were fine and I was free to travel. Glen and I drove to France for a golf tournament. I was looking forward to some sun and French culture: it was going to be fun caddying for Glen at his Alps Tour event.

When I woke up on the second day in our French cottage I knew something was wrong. My face was swollen and hot and the skin on my arms, neck and upper chest was so itchy and red. I still caddied for Glen and made sure I covered myself up from head to toe in long sleeves and trousers, hat and sunscreen. The sun was torture and just made the skin more tender and itchy. I 'slept' with wet cloths and damp cotton wool on my skin to try and keep the heat and itchiness at bay. I found an antihistamine at a local pharmacy despite still being unable to speak French, but it didn't have any effect. By the end of day three I was in agony and didn't know what to do with myself.

After a call to the Renal Unit in Brighton, we made the decision to stop taking the sirolimus. I was obviously reacting to it. The only anti-rejection medication I was left on was azathioprine. This was the lowest dose of immunosuppressant I had been on since the transplant. It was frightening. We had to get me home and fast. Without any other medication, the risk of rejection was huge.

Finally I agreed to a biopsy. It was the only way the medical team could assess the damage and decide on the best course of action. Otherwise they were effectively treating me blind. Being admitted to hospital was like stepping back in time. I was reminded that I was a kidney patient and always will be.

My consultant was amazing. He was really understanding of my fears and gave me a dose of happy drugs to cope with the procedure. I remember very little and felt no pain. Apparently I spoke a lot of rubbish and acted quite drunk. I had to remain flat on the bed for eight hours and spent the night in hospital again before being allowed home the next morning.

The results showed cyclosporin toxicity. Unfortunately there was some permanent scarring to the kidney but at least we had stopped any further damage. The problem I had now was that the range of possible drugs I could use had been reduced. I couldn't take sirolimus, cyclosporin or the newer Prograf, so that left prednisone, a steroid. As you know by now, I hate steroids, but prednisone is one of the simplest yet most effective transplant rejection drugs and has been around as long as azathioprine. It works on the immune system to help block allergic reactions and inflammation. However, it has numerous side effects, including increased appetite and weight gain, osteoporosis, muscle weakness, diabetes and thinning of the skin.

Within a day, I could taste the prednisone and a few hours after swallowing my morning dose I felt the tingling in my hands and the bitterness in mouth. I begged the doctors to take me off the drug or reduce the dosage faster, but I was fighting a losing battle. They had nothing else to give me.

Over time, I have learnt to handle the prednisone. I'm on such a low dose that I feel stupid for complaining. I now take it at night to avoid experiencing the bitter taste and the tingling hands. My thick, shiny hair has dried and thinned out. There were a few traumatic months of large clumps in my hands whenever I had a shower (a reaction to the change of medication) and my face has become slightly rounder. But the good news is that Bernie the Bean is happy and my creatinine has stabilised. In fact my blood results are better now than they have ever been and you can't argue with that! Complaining about side effects makes me feel vain and ungrateful. I want this kidney to last and I will do anything to make that happen

I started playing tennis again. This time at a local club near my home in West Sussex. It has been really great enjoying some of the success and fitness that I took for granted in my teens. At times it frustrates the hell out of me though: my body is just not as strong as it was and my skills are nowhere near as good. But Glen and I love the social aspects of the game and enjoy having a sport that we can play together, apart from golf.

Golf is still one of my passions and I am now a fair-weather golfer. I definitely prefer playing in the southern hemisphere, where rain is less likely and the sun shines more frequently. My best ever round came in 2003 at my final World Transplant Games event in Nancy, France, where I had a near perfect score. If it wasn't for a couple of loose shots and a bogey on the last hole I would have shot level par that day. I won the gold medal again – for Great Britain this time, as that was where I was living – and was proud to have the lowest score out of everyone who competed that afternoon, men as well as women.

After France I decided that I had achieved all I wanted to in the World Transplant Games. I had added squash and tennis to my list of sports and done well in those too, but it was time to move on. My life was taking on new focus and direction with my husband and career. The aim of the Games is to promote the incredible success of transplantation and to pay tribute to the countless organ donors who have made life possible for so many. I will always cherish the Games I took part in and am forever grateful for the inspiration and support they provided. They were the catalyst to helping me travel once more and rebuild my dreams.

*

The Observer **Wednesday August 13, 2003**　　　www.icsurrey

The sky's the limit for fundraising transplant heroine

by **Kelly Ranson**
kellyranson@trinitysouth.co.uk

AN INSPIRATIONAL woman who has just returned with a string of medals from the World Transplant Games is now gearing up for her next event.

Helen Philpott, from Newchapel Road, Lingfield, who underwent a kidney transplant, is preparing to jump out of an aeroplane in September to raise funds for the National Kidney Research Fund.

The 32-year-old had the transplant when she was just 20 years old - shattering her dream of becoming a professional tennis player.

Now, 11 years on, Helen, has just returned from the World Transplant Games in Nancy, France, with two gold medals for golf and squash and a bronze medal for tennis.

She said: "I was desperate to find a new goal after the transplant. I hit my first golf ball three months post transplant and was hooked.

"Since then I have managed to get my handicap down to an 8 and have won numerous gold medals at the World Games over the years."

Her mother Bernadine, who lives in East Grinstead, was Helen's kidney donor - something she will never forget.

Helen said: "To pay tribute to my mother after her generous gift of a kidney to me all those years ago, I am going to jump out of a plane."

"Having a kidney transplant changed my life.

"It got me off lifelong dialysis, gave me hope to live again and to accomplish so much more than I would have ever thought possible.

"I am now grateful for every opportunity and experiences that have come my way."

Anyone wanting more information on organ donation or kidney disease should contact National Kidney Research on 0845 300 1499.

● If you would like to sponsor Helen and other transplant receivers making the jump in September, then contact 07919 115 929.

Transplant success: Helen Philpott tees off at the World Transplant Games

Credit - The Observer, Surrey

Me, Christine (wife of the late Graham Marsh, my golfing friend who lived life fully with his new heart) and my friend Valerie from Australia (also a kidney recipient) enjoying the opening ceremony at the World Transplant Games in Nancy, France in 2003.

Winning my last gold for Golf at the World Transplant Games in Nancy, representing Great Britain and Northern Ireland

We celebrated the 20th anniversary of my kidney transplant in 2012. What an incredible milestone this was for me. Having lost my first kidney after just five months, every year with Bernie the Bean has been a bonus and a blessing.

Thanks to research and better medication regimes, the success rate for transplantations has improved over the years. Around ninety-five per cent of transplant patients now have a successful first year. The percentages go down slightly after that, but I think this is chiefly because the medical profession doesn't know how long a kidney could last. The longest-lasting recorded kidney transplant is over forty years. I have so many inspirational friends around the world who have had their kidneys for over twenty and even over thirty years. I have also lost so many friends around the world. Many of them were people I befriended at the World Transplant Games. It is always sad when someone loses their battle with kidney failure, but the message is invariably the same: transplantation gave them their lives back. Every one of them lived their life to the fullest. Thanks to the generosity of their donors, they were able to make a difference in the world, be with their families for longer, achieve goals they thought were out of reach and make time to enjoy the pleasures of life. Organ donation and transplantation truly saves lives. I know I wouldn't be here without it.

The weekend of 22 September 2012 was spent with my family, including my uncle Brian from America and my aunt and uncle from Yorkshire. We all gathered at an activity resort in Devon, England. We instigated the 'Philympics' and created a programme of sporting events including golf, short tennis, pool, bowls and target shooting to entertain us for the weekend. It was so lovely to spend this special time together, celebrating all that was made possible thanks to my transplant operation. I was able to pay tribute to my mother, who had made those last twenty years possible, and thank my family for their amazing love and support throughout. I couldn't have chosen a better way to celebrate life and all that I have enjoyed and experienced.

The family short tennis tournament at the Philympics in Devon.

Michelle and I about to tee off for the golf tournament of
the Philympics.

Mom and I celebrating 20 years since the transplant.

Celebrating our 20th anniversary of the transplant at the Philympics in Devon, England. From the left, me, Glen, Dad, Mom, Brian, Lawson, Chris, Jenny and Michelle.

Me, Mom and Michelle in 2013.

*

I'm a very different person now to the ambitious, self-absorbed eighteen-year-old tennis champ who jetted off to Louisiana with a head full of dreams. My priorities in life have changed enormously. Before kidney failure I was focused on myself but not on others. My priority was succeeding at school and more importantly at sport. All I wanted to do was play professional sport. Nothing else mattered. I was free to do what I wanted, when I wanted and was in full control of my destiny, or so I thought.

When my kidneys failed, my priority became survival. Nothing else seemed important. Life would go on around me but I was introspective and self-centred, fuelled by a steely determination to get over this major medical challenge. No one else mattered and my empathy for others was reduced. My friends and family must have felt this. I wasn't nasty, I just wasn't able to take much interest in other people's lives or concerns. My battle to overcome kidney failure was all-consuming and tough. It needed my full attention and energy.

Following my second transplant and the chance to live again, my priorities shifted once more. I started to see the world differently, woke up to the suffering of other people and wanted nothing more than to prevent others from having to go through the traumas of kidney failure or in fact any chronic illness. I realised that if I could share even a little of what I had learnt, I could help in my own way. I understood what it is like to face a life-threatening illness and one's own mortality. My passion to influence and change the way people view kidney health, medication, organ donation and transplantation has fuelled my desire to share this message through public speaking.

My priority also became to live life to the full and make the most of every day. I didn't suddenly start waking up with a grin on my face, although that certainly happened on some mornings; I just realised how precious life was and there was no way I was going to waste a minute of it being unhappy. This was my chance to make a difference in the world. If I could make any sense of why I had been struck down with kidney disease, then this was how. Even if I never found the answers, at least I could make the struggle worth it.

I no longer see sport as the driving force to success, however sport has given me so many amazing experiences and taught me so much. It continues to do so. My life is more balanced and I now focus on fulfilment and enjoyment rather than struggle and strife. There are so many moments when I think, man, I am lucky to be alive. I am reminded of this regularly – on the golf course; while powerwalking past London's Buckingham Palace; watching the sunset; wandering along a mile-long beach in Australia; striding up a hill with Jasper, my dog; drinking a latte in the sunshine with friends or enjoying a beautiful view with Glen. Who would have thought this possible for the kidney kid of twenty, who looked like she would be confined to dialysis for the rest of her life? If it wasn't for the miracle of transplantation I would most certainly not be here to tell the tale of Helen Philpott, now Haynes.

The future is bright. I hope Mom's kidney outlasts me. It is my aim to continue living life to the full – to make it count. Thank goodness for Mom, thank goodness for modern medicine and thank goodness I live in a time that has made all this possible. Medicine nearly destroyed me, but modern medicine has also saved me. I can say the same for people. There are so many who have touched my life, changed my life and made me who I am today. The list of those to thank is very long. The best way to pay tribute to them is to savour the love and happiness and do all that I can to make mine a life well lived.

Skiing in Chamonix, French Alps.

Jasper loves France. That's us in a ski lift in the French Alps.

I did achieve my goal of parasailing and enjoyed this exhilarating experience in Meribel, in the stunning French Alps.

Afterword

I know I am outspoken, honest and very determined. These traits are not always positively received but I am certain that without them I would not be alive today. They have kept me fighting through all the challenges I have had to face in my life and will continue to do so.

There is still plenty to achieve and lots I want to do. By sharing my message with the world, I want to raise awareness of kidney disease, transplantation and organ donation. It is my wish that treatments will continue to improve and one day there might even be a cure for kidney failure so that the many thousands of people on dialysis will be given hope for the future.

Glen and I share a love of travelling and together with our beloved dog, Jasper; we want to do much more exploring around the world. A few things on the bucket list include: visiting the Grand Canyon, seeing the Northern Lights, enjoying a week on Bora Bora, visiting the White House, and watching the sunset at Uluru. I also want to play golf to par and have a hole-in-one! But mostly, I just want to be completely happy, content in the knowledge that I have done my best and made this second chance count.

As I continue to strive to make a difference in the world, I believe that with the right attitude, self-belief and loving support, I can overcome anything.

Life is a journey. Struggles and triumphs are part of that tremendous journey. However, you need to believe that you can handle whatever challenges you face in order to relish living and find fulfilment and success in all you do.

I hope you've enjoyed my story and feel inspired to live your life fully, with determination to Make it Count!

Helen

August 2014

My Grateful Thanks

Writing a book is hard; however, writing my thanks to the many people who have supported me on my journey is not only hard but scary! I don't want to forget anyone and I really want you all to know how much I value and appreciate you.

Please forgive any omissions. This story is being shared from my point of view and all anecdotes, quotations and conversations are as remembered by me. I take full responsibility for any inaccuracies. Some names have been changed to protect individuals' privacy.

It has been an interesting (sometimes challenging) and emotional experience to reflect on my life and I am so grateful to everyone who has contributed and helped make this book a reality.

The book started over twenty years ago when Carol Suttner (wife of Ray) gave me a notebook and encouraged me to write my story. I thought she was totally crazy suggesting that there was a book in me, but I am glad she had so much faith. Let's hope it lives up to your expectations, Carol. Sorry it has taken so long!

Starting a book is a daunting task and only when I met the talented Lindiwe Dovey did I begin to believe that it might be possible. Lindi helped shape my story and developed a structure for me to build on. She was based in Sydney and spent hours interviewing me and sending questions and answers back and forth via email (in those days we had dial-up, so it was pretty slow); finally we even lived together for a month, when I moved to Sydney. I am so grateful to you, Lindi, for your creativity and hard work. It meant a great deal and still much of your writing shines through.

I had a number of people read my drafts and provide comments and suggestions for improvement. The late Carmel Kremmer believed in my story and gave me valuable comments; I'm so sorry she isn't with us to enjoy the read. Thank you also to Kim

McClenaghan for your writer's wisdom and pertinent questions; you kept me thinking and pushed me to show not tell. And to Walton Woodford for your words of encouragement before I finally took the plunge to publish, thank you.

Finding book coach Wendy Yorke to get me over the last hurdles was such a blessing. I couldn't have asked for a more positive, inspiring or motivating individual. She encouraged me all the way. Wendy, your enthusiasm, coaching skills and support were incredible. Your goal was to get me published and you got me there – thank you!

My publisher Chris Day and his team at Filament have made the publishing process so much easier. Thank you for putting up with all my questions and patiently explaining everything over numerous coffees and calls. It's been a pleasure working with someone so passionate about books and so knowledgeable about publishing. Let's hope the book is a success.

I believe that the key to quality writing is finding the right editor and I have most definitely found the right person in Lucy Ridout. Thank you, Lucy, for 'getting me' and helping me share my story in the best possible way. Your patience and skill have been amazing. I have loved working with you and am so grateful to have had someone I trust and believe in to help deliver the book in just the right way.

Thank you to Simon at The Image Cella for your brilliant creativity with the camera and to Sylvia and Sam for making me look good for the photo shoot.

During the writing of this book I have reconnected with so many old and wonderful friends, doctors and colleagues. I've been overwhelmed by the kind words of encouragement and support. Thank you all for making me feel special.

Thank you to everyone who has helped me to live my bonus years to the best of my ability. In particular I want to acknowledge some really special friends who have given me so much love, support and laughter over the years. Due to the nature of the story, you don't feature in this book, but this does not diminish your importance in my life; we are another story altogether. Joan and Gordon - you may as well be my adopted godparents because you are more like family than friends – thank you for everything! Mike and Fi, Jacs and Scott, Jeff and Judy, Ings, Damo, Val, Sydney Sue, Melbourne Sue (what an inspiration you are!) and Lisa – all of you have made life in Australia so special – I love you guys! Alan (my oldest and closest sporting friend – tennis, golf, skiing and snowboarding – what next?), Stan (who is more like a brother), Sally, Helen Bear (my fundraising namesake who is such a support) and Sarah, my friend and PR advisor. My life has been richer for knowing you all.

I would also like to pay special tribute to my first organ donor, whose family generously allowed his organs to be donated, giving me hope for a future and at least five months of freedom from dialysis. That meant so much and I wished with all my heart that it would be for life.

My medical team was second to none. I can't thank Dr G and the Renal Unit team at the Frere Hospital enough: your care and skill were extraordinary. Thanks also go to the Renal and Transplant team at Groote Schuur in Cape Town – you guys were groundbreaking, creative and extremely determined to pull me through. I will never know how you all put up with me. I questioned everything, pushed you to look at every option and challenged the medical profession in every way possible. One thing was for sure: we were on the same side and together we fought like hell. There was no way I was going to let kidney failure get the better of me. It had chosen the wrong woman.

Finally my grateful thanks go to my family. Michelle and Peter, you have been such fantastic, long-suffering siblings, not least during those four years when you had to take a back seat in our family drama. Thank you Mich and Chris for giving me such a beautiful niece. Mim and Lincs (my new family), thank you for all your kindness and, of course, my gorgeous Aussie niece. I love being an Aunt! Jen and Lawson, my aunt and uncle, thank you for your love and support. Mom and Dad, you have always made sure that we had all we needed to make a success of our lives. Thank you for leading by example and encouraging us to make the most of every opportunity and ensure we live life to the full. Your love and support was the motivation I needed to keep fighting. We have been through some fantastic times and some challenging times, but we are always there for each other, no matter where we are in the world. Your love and constant support means so much. Thank you for allowing me to share this story with the world.

Glen, my tolerant and wonderful husband, thank you for giving me time and space to finish this book - it has made all the difference. Thank you for loving me just the way I am. How lucky am I to have found my soul mate? I love you!

This book is for all of you and in particular for Mom and Dad: Mom for giving me the incredible gift of life and Dad for your unending love and support.

My wonderful family with Joan and Gordon and my uncle Brian.

A Message from My Mom – the Real Hero of This Story

As a young child, Helen already showed signs of being a champion – whatever she did, she did to the best of her ability so it was no surprise that she achieved her aim to attend an American University on a tennis scholarship.

When, after only one year, ill-health forced her to return to South Africa, we had no idea that we were about to embark on a rollercoaster journey that would change our lives for ever. Our close-knit family was often torn apart as I spent much time in Cape Town at Helen's bedside praying and hoping that she would survive. All this would not have been possible without the help and support of our incredible friends, family and colleagues who not only helped us financially but visited and phoned us regularly. At times it was difficult to constantly answer their questions about the state of Helen's health, but we appreciated all the caring and prayers that came our way.

While Helen's story gives an account of all the many scary, painful experiences and ups and downs she faced, it hopefully will also highlight her inner strength, determination and dogged persistence never to give up. Her unwavering belief in the fact that she would survive helped me cope during some of the darkest hours. I learnt to take one day at a time and am thankful for the additional 22 years that the transplant has already given Helen – proving that transplantation does work.

Her suffering taught me never to take things for granted, that the medical profession are not infallible and that we have a right to question their actions. Helen constantly demanded explanations and tried to take control of what was happening to her – this probably saved her life on more than one occasion.

People with kidney disease, even after a transplant, face uncertain futures, but by living each day to the fullest and striving to make a difference, Helen's message to 'Make it Count!' will hopefully inspire others.

I am proud of the way Helen strives to make that difference - she is my Champion!

- Bernadine Philpott

Messages Of Support

'It is hard to imagine now what Helen and our family were going through all those years ago. We look back now and realise what strength and determination Helen had (and still has).

The caring and generous support of the East London community will never be forgotten.

Helen has really made the most of her second chance in life and I am sure anyone reading her book will be motivated in the same way.

We are so proud of her achievements and know she will succeed in all that she undertakes. She is an inspiration to us all – enjoy her story.'

- Michael Philpott
Helen's Dad

*

'Helen is a remarkable young woman who makes an immediate, positive impression on all whom she meets. A warm, effervescent person, Helen thrives in the company of people. Having faced considerable personal adversity, Helen has triumphed against the odds because of her unique courage, sense of purpose and an incredible will to win. As a result of her personal drive she has achieved a great deal in her life.'

- The late Ray Suttner
Former Director of Rhodes University, East London

'My memory of my first encounter with Helen all those years ago was of a young sportswoman (tennis player) who had the potential for a very successful career ahead of her but was affected by kidney failure and needed a kidney transplant. I was amazed at how this setback did not deter her and she continued to live her life as normally as possible after the transplant. I was a little jealous of how good a golfer she was even after the transplant. Helen has remained enormously positive throughout all the ups and downs, and one can only admire her for this.'

- Del Kahn
Head of the Department of Surgery
University of Cape Town and Groote Schuur Hospital

*

'Helen displayed a natural all-round sporting ability from an early age and we were thrilled when she joined our gym club, knowing that ball games were more entrenched in the family! Through sheer hard work and dedication she was able to improve her suppleness and dancing ability to rival any of her team mates. Helen was known to practise the splits every night after her bath! She was the perfect gymnast who always listened well.

Both Tubby and I loved coaching this determined little girl with the huge grin and a lovely sense of fun. We always believed that gymnastics provided a wonderful grounding for children and the coordination skills, self-discipline, desire and courage would put them in good stead for any future sport they chose to pursue. This was proven in Helen's case as she became an outstanding tennis and hockey player. (And golfer too!)

Helen is an amazing young woman and Tubby and I feel privileged to have been part of her life for a few years.'

- Wendy and Tubby Usher
Gym Coaches

'I worked with Helen over a number of years when helping to raise much-needed funds for the new Teenage Cancer Trust unit in Southampton. I think the best way to describe her is by using three words: persuasive, motivating and kind. I turned up one dreary evening to a closed College of Further Education cafeteria, thinking I could possibly advise the fledgling charitable committee on how to market themselves – by the end of the meeting, Helen had not only persuaded me to join the committee, but I walked out the Chairman, which went on for four fun and highly rewarding years. Throughout the ups and the many downs (due to working on such an intense and emotive cause), she was on hand to focus us, inspire us and nurture us. She really changed my life.'

- Jay Aylmer
Managing Director
The Potting Shed Design and Advertising, Guernsey

*

'As a very good friend and associate of Helen's mother, Bernadine, I watched Helen grow up in a warm and loving family. During her teenage years, Helen developed into a very determined and driven sportswoman, with her eyes set firmly on a career in the sporting world.

It was with terrible sadness and dismay that I witnessed the cruel blow dealt to her dreams, but I saw in her, once again, that very determined young lady - this time to overcome her physical disabilities and carry on with a meaningful life.

This she has done in full measure, not only helping many of the physically less fortunate to live better lives, but in carving out a career for herself of which anyone could be proud.'

- Sybil Gersowsky
Former President of Border Hockey

(Kim McClenaghan, the oldest of the Mac siblings, was terrified of hospitals. Unlike the rest of his family, he could only bring himself to visit me once in Groote Schuur. He found that experience so terrifying that he wrote this poem about it.)

Groote Schuur – G13

I trod with trepidation pressing me
As the shuddering walls closed in,
      Pounding to the steady beat
      of the hospital's giant heart.

Four miles deep, it seemed,
Through passages, like veins
Pulsating up and down.
Four miles down from fresh air
That wasn't still with the smell of sickness.
Lungs flamed with the burn of antiseptic.

The windows were glazed eyes
Staring at the world outside,
      With tears.
Lights that were made by man
To try to hide the darkness
In some non-existent recess
Of fear itself.

The sound of silence is heavy
As it hovers like a thick blanket of fog
Knee-deep in the passages
And engulfs all in anguished groans.
It sneaks in sheets
      Through wards, like wombs
            That encase patients,
                  To sap souls away.

As soon as I left the breeze
And swayed into the still coldness,
I felt the mercurial injection of fear
     Take control
And anaesthetize my senses to numbness
As terror coiled up within me
     In revulsion,
To leave me quivering
     Waxen white
     As I looked at you
     And marveled
     At you who could.

I needed to run to the opening
Of this underground mine of misery –
Get out and scream at open air
As walls ceased their hold over and around me,
And tendrils of fear peeled off in the wind.

And I was able to run
     And jump
        And shout
           For you,
     And all the others who can't.

- Kim McClenaghan 10/09/93
For Helen

*

223

'We first met Helen when we went to London to find out about Teenage Cancer Trust and to see if it was something that our charitable foundation would consider supporting. After a couple of hours with Helen we had made a commitment to anchor the project to build a new unit for teenagers with cancer at Southampton hospital. At the time it was the largest single donation that we had ever made. At our next meeting I was persuaded to become a Patron of the Teenage Cancer Trust Appeal.

One of the early fundraising events was a concert at Winchester Cathedral. I had naively assumed that Helen, as the organiser, would be stuck at the back so I invited her to sit in the posh seats at the front. She politely declined, with all the grace and charm in the world. Ten minutes later, who was compere of the whole event? Helen of course! Eat your heart out Graham Norton and Jonathan Ross. Helen was amazing!

We first saw the 'caring' side of the charity at a reception at No 11 Downing Street. Nicole Dryburgh was launching her appeal to raise £100,000 for the charity. Helen was giving tremendous support to Nicole's family, way beyond the call of duty of a fundraising manager, and was courageously helping Nicole in her fight against cancer.

Helen is one of those people who will always give a positive response however crazy the idea. From life-sized dinosaur walks to jewellery launches in the Channel Islands – she was always up for a challenge. Together we fulfilled our mission of starting a charity appeal in Guernsey alongside her successful appeal in Jersey. She secured the support of Channel TV and raised the profile of the charity across the Channel Islands.

When Helen shared her history - South Africa, USA, tennis, kidney failure, transplant - I realised that she was a pretty unusual person with guts and determination to fight some incredible setbacks.

Even though Helen has now moved on from TCT we have celebrated our success of working together on many occasions and have many fond and happy memories of this effervescent, enthusiastic and dare I say, exhausting (in the nicest possible way) woman.'

- Geoff Squire, OBE

*

'It has been a tremendous honour and great privilege to help Helen, through coaching, to achieve her book publication goal and to support her on her journey of sharing her story to help others. I applaud her inspirational determination to succeed whatever the challenge and I know the message of her book will help others to overcome adversity and go for whatever it is they want out of their lives. Helen continues to shine even after all the storms she has been through in her life. She is a wonderful example of living in the present - with passion, energy, drive, focus and above all - an infectious sense of enjoyment!'

- Wendy Yorke,
Book Coach and Friend

*

'East London and Border has always possessed an intimate, rich sporting history, blessed with brilliant schools' leadership and teacher excellence. Its support structures and environment lend itself to a healthy, balanced education for tomorrow's champions. The young Helen Philpott is a product of this Border sporting mecca. Her parents, Mike and Bernadine, were creative in this embryo of academic and sporting wellbeing.

Helen's passion and talent was invested in tennis. She loved it. Her dream was Wimbledon – the US, French and Australian Open were on the agenda too. An American University Tennis Scholarship was her opportunity to sharpen the competitive, physical, technical skills required. Sometimes the desire to 'make the team' in a competitive league can obscure reality and Helen's overuse of anti-inflammatory medication to treat injuries sadly proved to be career-ending for her.

As Border Cricket captain and Rhodes University (East London Branch) Sports Development Director (1990 – 1993), I became teammates with Helen in an administrative and coaching/ motivation capacity to grow sports performance at this small faculty. The visionary behind this was the late Ray Suttner.

It was a pleasure working together as our love of sport and people dominated. Her enthusiasm and tremendous attitude was infectious, despite the loss of her tennis career at such an early age. Selflessly, she channeled her passion for sport into creating new horizons for the students. When diagnosed with kidney failure, her world changed and there was despair amongst us all. At the end of year Sports Dinner, still vivid in my memory, amid heartwarming applause Helen received the Award for her contribution to sport – it was most surely also for courage.

Helen Haynes is a unique, stoic character, mentally equipped to conquer a life-threatening situation, blessed with loving support. Hers is an inspiring story. I am pleased our paths crossed, although too briefly.'

- Peter Kirsten
Former Western Province, Border,
South African International Cricketer

*

'In the 1988 Final School Year Journal, of Hudson Park High School, situated in the small city of East London, South Africa, written by school pupils, the following was said of Helen: "Helen Philpott, a sports fanatic, was justly rewarded by being selected as captain of both the first hockey and tennis teams, as well as achieving her Border (Provincial) Colours and School Honours awards in both sports. She wishes to study for a career involving sport, preferably on a sports scholarship to the USA, or Stellenbosch University. She was a school prefect and achieved numerous merit awards, as well as Eagle and Service Awards."

Helen was also selected to join the South African Schools hockey squad, and was placed in the sprints at the school's athletic championships. In addition she was awarded the prize at the end of her high school career for being "The Most All-Round Pupil". The Eagle Award, mentioned above, is one awarded to a pupil who achieves exceptionally well in all four areas of school life - Academic, Cultural, Physical and Pastoral. The pupils who achieved the prestigious Eagle Award, were seen to embody the philosophy of the school. Helen certainly did!

What Helen has achieved since she left school is merely a continuation of achieving her potential, which she started as a young schoolgirl. She did achieve her goal of being awarded a scholarship to attend a University in the United States to further her budding tennis career.

Unfortunately, this is what also eventually led to her kidney failure and the end of her sporting dreams.

One would have thought this devastating occurrence would have affected Helen's achievements as an adult. Instead it led to a rethink of her future and the direction her life would take. It did not affect her will to succeed in her chosen career. Others, and this book, will testify to her successful fundraising for charitable organisations, her own public speaking career and her coaching and training of others to do the same.

I was privileged to witness the development and growth of this extremely talented young lady during the last five years of her schooling. I never doubted her strength to overcome any adversity and it has been done so with aplomb! She always has a smile on her face and an encouraging word for others. She has been fortunate to have the advice and support of her parents, Bernadine and Mike Philpott who have both achieved amazingly well in their own careers.

I know you will enjoy Helen's book. It is amusing, brutally honest, filled with enthusiasm and refreshing, as is Helen!'

- Peter Miles
Former Headmaster, Hudson Park High School
East London, South Africa

*

'I first met Helen early in 2002 as a single figure handicap golfer who was looking to improve a "little". I didn't realise at the time just what she meant by a "little"!

It wasn't long into our lessons that I started to appreciate precisely how driven and determined she was. On discovering what Helen had to endure, it was obvious to see where this energy and desire came from.

We worked together for a season, and I believe Helen could have achieved her goal of professional golf, but her overriding passion to help others less fortunate simply took over.

Helen has been extremely successful as an international fundraiser as well as within her business.

I have no doubt that overcoming her own difficulties so tirelessly, has given her the passion and commitment to succeed...and long may it continue.'

- Clive Tucker
European Tour Golf Coach

Organ Donation and Transplantation

O rgan donation gives seriously ill people with organ failure the chance of a new life. Transplantation is one of the miracles of modern medicine.

The kidneys, heart, liver, lungs, pancreas and small bowel, as well as other parts of the body such as eyes, skin, bone, tendons, cartilage and heart valves can all be donated.

The organ most commonly donated by a living person is a kidney. A healthy person can lead a normal life with only one functioning kidney and so is able to donate the other. Kidneys transplanted from living donors have a better chance of long-term survival than those transplanted from people who have died. You can also plan the transplant so that the recipient is at their healthiest and strongest and, if possible, still at an early stage of their dialysis treatment or even before dialysis.

Part of a liver can also be transplanted from a living donor.

The first successful kidney transplant was performed in 1954 in Boston, USA. Nowadays, around 3,200 kidney transplants are performed annually in the UK. Success of transplantation is reliant on immunosuppressant medication and now there is at least an 85 per cent success rate after ten years.

If you do wish to be considered for organ donation at the time of your death, adding your name to the Organ Donor Register will enable healthcare professionals to carry out your donation decisions. It will also make your family's decision easier at a very difficult time. Discuss your wishes with them while you can.

There is still a desperate need for organs all around the world. In the UK there are around 7,000 people waiting for organ transplants at any one time, over 5,000 of them waiting for kidneys. Up to three people die every day waiting for a life-saving organ. One organ donor can save up to nine people.

For more information on becoming an organ donor in the United Kingdom visit www.organdonation.nhs.uk.

Kidney Disease

Millions of people are at risk of chronic kidney disease (CKD), which can progress to be a serious condition for which there is no cure. Chronic kidney disease (CKD) is a long-term condition which involves any damage or abnormality in the kidneys. At its mildest, it can be almost undetectable. However, an important minority of people go on to develop end stage renal failure, which is fatal without dialysis treatment or a kidney transplant.

The signs are often difficult to spot which is why kidney disease is often referred to as the 'silent killer'. The people most likely to be at risk are those who suffer from diabetes, high blood pressure or heart disease. The condition can affect all age groups and is extremely common in older people. In most cases, CKD does not cause any symptoms and is detected because blood and urine tests are abnormal.

Kidney Transplantation

If you are diagnosed with failing kidneys, treatment can sometimes prevent (or certainly delay) their complete failure. But when your kidneys finally stop working effectively, then you will need either dialysis or a transplant. While dialysis is able to get rid of waste products from your body, it does not replace all the functions of your own kidneys. A transplant does. These necessary functions include:

- continuous removal of waste products and excess fluid
- production of a natural hormone called erythropoietin, to prevent anaemia
- conversion of vitamin D in food into an active compound, which helps to keep bones healthy

- excretion of some drugs
- helping to control blood pressure

Your kidneys are normally undertaking these functions continuously, day and night, year in year out, without you even having to think about it.

It has been shown that kidney transplantation gives better quality and quantity of life than dialysis treatment, so if you are fit enough to undergo this procedure it offers you the best chance of successful treatment.

To find out more about kidney disease visit:
www.kidneyresearchuk.org

Get in Touch

Please feel free to get in touch or find me online.
I would love to hear how this book has inspired
you in some way, or just write to say 'hello'.

Email: helen@helenhaynes.co.uk
Twitter: @helen_haynes
Facebook: www.facebook.com/helenmakesitcount
Website: www.helenhaynes.co.uk